a
las
penal

ANDRZEJ MOSTOWSKI

THIRTY YEARS OF
FOUNDATIONAL STUDIES

LECTURES ON THE DEVELOPMENT OF
MATHEMATICAL LOGIC AND THE STUDY OF
THE FOUNDATIONS OF MATHEMATICS
IN 1930—1964

OXFORD
BASIL BLACKWELL
1966

ACTA PHILOSOPHICA FENNICA

FASC. XVII

Printed in Finland
Suomalaisen Kirjallisuuden Kirjapaino Oy Helsinki 1965

225011

Contents

Foreword

In the summer of 1964 I delivered in the Summer School in Vaasa, Finland, a series of lectures on the development of mathematical logic and of the study of foundations of mathematics in the years 1930—1964. The subject was suggested to me by the Rector of the School, Professor Oiva Ketonen.

When preparing these lectures I had to evaluate critically the period to which my whole scientific activity belongs. As this retrospection turned out to be an exciting mental experiment I accepted with gratitude the proposal of Professors Ketonen, Hintikka and von Wright to work out my lectures and to publish them in the series *Acta Philosophica Fennica*.

A review like the present one can be neither entirely impartial nor entirely complete. The choice of the subjects which one wants to take up thus presents considerable difficulties. Further difficulties arise when one tries to give a concise characterisation of various discoveries and of their mutual relations. The task becomes still incomparably more difficult when one has to express oneself in a foreign language. Only after the completion of the work does one see how far it falls short of the image one had in mind when one started it. If in spite of the difficulties I have decided to publish the lectures, I did it in the hope that they may convey to the (rare) reader some of the enthusiasm with which I witnessed the creation of theories reported on in the following pages.

In addition to the Editors of the *Acta Philosophica Fennica*, my thanks are due to the Vaasa Summer School, to its Rector, Professor Ketonen, and to the group of Finnish and Swedish students whose sympathetic collaboration made me feel that the task of preparing these lectures was perhaps not quite useless.

ANDRZEJ MOSTOWSKI

Introduction

Our aim in these lectures is to sketch the development of mathematical logic and of the study of foundations of mathematics in the years 1930—1964. It will not be possible to enter into the details of all the theories that have been created during this period; we shall, rather, content ourselves with brief indications of their contents and of their applications. Thus the presentation will of necessity be somewhat superficial. We believe, however, that it may nevertheless have some interest as it covers a wide field and thus enables one to see the work done in the last few decades in a wide perspective.

It is customary to distinguish three major movements in the philosophy of mathematics: the intuitionism of Brouwer, the logicism of Frege and Russell and the formalism of Hilbert. The first of them views mathematics in isolation from other branches of science and insists on restricting the notions and methods used in mathematics to the most elementary and intuitive ones. For these reasons, few mathematicians have joined the intuitionistic school. The logicism of Frege and Russell tries to reduce mathematics to logic. This seemed to be an excellent program, but when it was put into effect, it turned out that there is simply no logic strong enough to encompass the whole of mathematics. Thus what remained from this program is a reduction of mathematics to set theory. This can hardly be said to be a satisfactory solution of the problem of foundations of mathematics since among all mathematical theories it is just the theory of sets that requires clarification more than any other. Finally, the formalism of Hilbert sets up a program which requires, first that the whole of mathematics be axiomatised and, secondly, that these axiomatic theories be then proved consistent by using very simple combinatorial arguments. As it has turned out, this program is not realizable; and even if it were, it would hardly satisfy philosophically minded mathematicians because of the inevitable arbitrariness of the axioms.

The philosophical aims of the three schools have thus not been achieved, and it seems to us that we are no nearer to a complete understanding of mathematics than the founders of these schools. In spite of this, it cannot be denied that the activity of these schools has brought about a great number of important new insights and discoveries which have deepened our knowledge of mathematics and its relation to logic. As it often happens, these by-products have turned out to be more important than the original aims of the founders of the three schools. It will be our aim to study these results so as to obtain a picture of how the philosophical programs of the three major schools have influenced the formal development of logic and of the foundational study. We will see that the contribution of each of them has been great and that none of them could exist without the others.

The three schools underwent great changes during the years 1930 —1960. Especially striking has been the development of meta-mathematics which originally aimed at a proof of consistency as envisaged by Hilbert but which has later developed into a much more ambitious theory. The most important results of meta-mathematics have their origin in certain studies started in the early thirties. It is true that these results have discredited in part the philosophical program of the formalist school, but it is also true that the meta-mathematical discoveries have revolutionised our knowledge of mathematics and of formal logic.

Intuitionism has not changed its basic philosophy but has begun to change its formal side. Formulae, which were previously banned altogether, have replaced in part the complicated and often incomprehensible verbal expressions used in older publications. In this way intuitionistic theories, which were previously known almost exclusively in the narrow circle of the followers of Brouwer, became intelligible to other philosophers and mathematicians, to a great benefit of both sides. There also appeared other theories not directly connected with intuitionism but sharing with it the tendency to restrict mathematical notions to very simple ones. Collectively, these theories are known as the constructivistic trend in the modern philosophy of mathematics. Intuitionism in the proper sense of the word is probably the most interesting of these constructivistic theories.

Logicism, which dominated foundational studies in the years prior to 1930, did not create essentially new conceptions after 1930.

There were scholars, *e.g.* Leśniewski, who worked essentially along the lines of the old program of the logicists, but their influence has been small. The program of logicism nevertheless survived in the guise of set-theoretical conceptions. This is only natural if we reflect that type theory and other similar systems to which the logicists tried to reduce mathematics were essentially axiomatic systems of the abstract theory of sets.

Thus we shall have to account for the contributions of the following three main schools of thought: the constructivistic, the meta-mathematical and the set-theoretical. In the early thirties appeared three publications which can be taken to be representative of these three schools and which greatly influenced their further development. These were the well-known works by Heyting [80], Gödel [54] and Tarski [222]. We shall begin our exposition by discussing these papers and certain other works which immediately depend on them.

Lecture I

Formalization of the intuitionistic logic

Intuitionism as invented by Brouwer rests on several general principles, only some of which are relevant to intuitionistic logic. Very important but not relevant to our immediate purpose is the assumption that general set-theoretical notions are not to be admitted into mathematics and that all mathematics is to be reduced to the arithmetic of integers and to a very special intuitionistic theory of the continuum. Another no less important assumption which is very relevant to intuitionistic logic is the intuitionistic contention that logic does not precede mathematics but is a result of the mathematical activity. A law of logic is, according to this thesis, a form of deduction which has been accepted by mathematicians; before mathematicians have used deductions of this form there was no reason to accept it as a law of logic. Finally, a third thesis prescribes certain forms of reasoning which according to intuitionists are the only ones to be admitted into mathematics. Mathematicians, so says the thesis, can only perform certain (mental) constructions; a mathematical theorem is but a report on these constructions.

In order to make this point clearer let us consider the following situation. Suppose that a mathematician tries to prove the existence of an object with some prescribed properties. In order to do this he performs certain constructions, and if he succeeds in obtaining in this way an object with the requisite properties, then he has proved an intuitionistically admissible existential statement. Let us now suppose that our mathematician has failed to construct directly an object as required, but that he can derive a contradiction from the assumption that there are no objects with the requisite properties. A classical logician would still say that an existential statement has been proved by our mathematician, but an intuitionist would deny this. According to the intuitionistic conception, the proof of impossibility which was carried out by our mathematician is a construction showing the impossibility of proving the general statement: "Every x is deprived of the properties in question"; it is not a construction of an object satisfying these properties. Hence the negation of a general statement is not equivalent to an existential statement. We see from this example that the identification of a mathematical theorem with a construction leads us to reject certain laws of classical logic. As it happens, the formulae which are accepted by intuitionists are true under the classical interpretation; thus intuitionistic logic is a proper part of classical logic.

Heyting [80] was the first to undertake a formalization of intuitionistic logic. He divided his system into two parts, one dealing with propositional logic and the other with the logic of quantification. We shall present here the propositional logic of Heyting's in a slightly modified form.

The primitive notions of this system are: alternation (denoted by $\vee$), conjunction (denoted by $\wedge$), implication (denoted by $\to$) and the constant F denoting a false sentence. The axioms for alternation and conjunction are the same as in classical logic:

$$\text{(A)} \quad p \to (p \vee q), \quad q \to (p \vee q), \quad (p \to r) \to \{(q \to r) \to [(p \vee q) \to r]\},$$

$$\text{(K)} \quad (p \wedge q) \to p, \quad (p \wedge q) \to q, \quad (r \to p) \to \{(r \to q) \to [r \to (p \wedge q)]\}.$$

The axioms for the connective $\to$ and for the constant F constitute only a part of the corresponding classical axioms:

$$\text{(I)} \quad [p \to (q \to r)] \to [(p \to q) \to (p \to r)], \quad p \to (q \to p),$$

$$\text{(F)} \qquad\qquad\qquad\qquad F \to p.$$

The only rule of inference is the classical *modus ponens*. The equivalence $p \equiv q$ is defined as $(p \to q) \wedge (q \to p)$ and the negation $\neg p$ as $p \to F$.

The system characterized by the axioms (I) is known as positive implicational logic; the axioms (A), (K), (I) characterize the full positive logic. Not all classically true formulae which involve only the connective $\to$ are derivable from (I); they are derivable from (I) together with the axiom known as Peirce's law:

$$\text{(P)} \qquad\qquad\qquad [(p \to q) \to p] \to p.$$

The axioms (A), (K), (I), (F), (P) are sufficient for the derivation of all classically true propositional formulae. Indeed, by substituting F for q in (P) we obtain the formula

(i) $$(\neg p \to p) \to p.$$

From (I) we can derive easily the formula $p \to [(p \to q) \to q]$ which upon substitution $q = F$ gives us $p \to (\neg p \to F)$, whence according to (F)

(ii) $$p \to (\neg p \to q).$$

Finally, the law of syllogism

(iii) $$(p \to q) \to [(q \to r) \to (p \to r)]$$

is easily derivable from (I). Thus all the axioms of the well known system of Łukasiewicz are derivable from (I), (F), and (P). Since the formulae $(p \lor q) \equiv (\neg p \to q)$, $(p \land q) \equiv \neg (p \to \neg q)$ are easily derivable from (A), (K), and the classical laws for $\to$ and $\neg$, we see that (A), (K), (I), (F), (P) are indeed sufficient for the derivation of all the laws of the classical propositional logic.

Peirce's law (P) is far from being intuitively obvious. The intuitionistic axioms (A), (K), (I), (F) are, on the contrary, very clear and intuitive. We conclude that the intuitionistic logic is simpler and more natural than the classical one.

In order to obtain the logic of quantifiers from the propositional logic we proceed exactly as in the classical case: we add the axioms

(Q) $$\bigwedge_x Fx \to Fy, \qquad Fy \to \bigvee_x Fx$$

and the following rules of proof:

$$\frac{A \to Fx}{A \to \bigwedge_x Fx} \qquad \frac{Fx \to A}{\bigvee_x Fx \to A}$$

where A is a formula which does not contain x as a free variable.

The above method of formalizing intuitionistic logic does not differ essentially from the one proposed by Heyting. There are other ways, perhaps more elegant ones, of formalizing this logic, *e.g.* the very simple method of Gentzen [50]; we shall not, however, enter into the details of these other methods.

Several important meta-mathematical theorems about the formalized intuitionistic logic were discovered soon after Heyting published his paper. The most interesting one was the discovery made by Gödel [56], based in part on some earlier results of Glivenko [52], that the classical logic can be interpreted in the intuitionistic one. Gödel defined new connectives $\sim, +, \cdot, \supset$ by means of the equations
$$\sim p = \neg p, \quad p \cdot q = p \wedge q, \quad p + q = \sim(\sim p \cdot \sim q), \quad p \supset q = \sim(p \cdot \sim q),$$
and showed that if we replace in any formula the connectives $\neg, \wedge, \vee, \rightarrow$ by $\sim, \cdot, +, \supset$, then all the classically true formulae will go over into intuitionistically provable formulae, whereas formulae which are not classically true go over into formulae which are not intuitionistically provable. In order to obtain an analogous result for the logic of quantifiers we may interpret the existential quantifier as $\neg \bigwedge_x \neg$ and leave the general quantifier unchanged.

In this way Gödel proved that the classical logic is faithfully representable in the intuitionistic logic. Of course the intuitionistic logic is identically interpretable in the classical logic, but this identical interpretation is not a faithful one.

Gödel showed that the same relationship exists between certain axiomatic theories based on the classical and the intuitionistic logic. Thus *e.g.* Peano's arithmetic based on the classical logic is interpretable in Peano's arithmetic based on the intuitionistic logic. This theorem gives us an intuitionistic consistency proof for Peano's arithmetic based on the classical logic. It is remarkable that this proof should turn out to be so easy while no strictly finitistic consistency proof exists. Peano's arithmetic based on the intuitionistic logic contains thus many non-finitistic elements.

Much effort was devoted by logicians and mathematicians to attempts to obtain a classical interpretation of the intuitionistic logic. Results in this direction evidently do not interest intuitionists who do not have to interpret their own logic in the classical system, which is unintelligible to them. For people who adhere to classical logic an interpretation is the only method which allows them to understand intuitionistic logic.

A very interesting interpretation was given by Kolmogorov, who interpreted the intuitionistic logic as the logic of problems. The connectives $\neg, \vee, \wedge, \rightarrow$ are interpreted as operations of forming a new problem out of given ones. *E.g.* the implication $p \rightarrow q$ is the problem which consists of reducing the problem q to the problem p. Intuitionistic identities built up by means of the connectives and the variables p, q, r, . . . will then represent schemata of problems which admit solutions independently of the particular choice of p, q, r, . . . This interpretation is well in keeping with the intuitionistic conception that a mathematical theorem is always identical with a (theoretical) construction.

More influential than this interpretation was another one devised by Tarski [225]. A very similar conception was also published about the same time by Stone [218].

A close connection between the classical propositional calculus and the calculus of classes had been known since the time of Boole. The parallelism between these calculi is best seen when one uses the same symbols for propositional connectives and for operations on sets; we have then *e.g.* the equivalences $[x \in (X \vee Y)] \equiv [(x \in X)$ $\vee (x \in Y)]$, $(x \in \neg X) \equiv \neg (x \in X)$, *etc.* To each propositional formula we can then associate a Boolean polynomial simply by interpreting the propositional variables as set-variables ranging over all the subsets of an arbitrary set V. The classical logical identities are associated with those polynomials whose value is V independently of the values given to the variables. This interpretation is no longer valid for the intuitionistic logic since *e.g.* the intuitionistically unprovable formula $p \vee \neg p$ is associated with a polynomial whose value is V for every p. The problem formulated by Tarski was to find a class $\boldsymbol{G}$ of subsets of V and suitable operations performable on these subsets such that the following be true: If we correlate with a propositional formula a polynomial obtained by interpreting the connectives as these operations on sets and the propositional variables as arbitrary sets in $\boldsymbol{G}$ we obtain a polynomial identically equal to V if and only if the formula we started with is intuitionistically provable. Tarski showed that we can take as V a suitable topological space, *e.g.* a Euclidean plane, as $\boldsymbol{G}$ the class of open subsets of V, and interpret F as the void set and the connectives $\vee$, $\wedge$, $\rightarrow$ as union, intersection and as the operation $Int \ [(V - X) \cup Y]$, respectively. Open sets are of course those subsets of V which together with any point p contain a sufficiently small neighbourhood of p. $Int \ (A)$ is the interior of A, *i.e.* the largest open set contained in A.

Let us discuss an example of a topological space. Let T be a finite directed tree, *i.e.* a set of points called vertices some of which are connected by directed edges in such a way that there are no closed cycles. (For examples of such trees, see diagrams 1 and 2.)

Diagram 1.   Diagram 2.

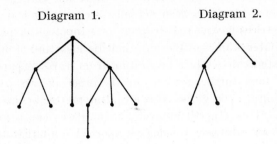

Each tree T of the sort just described has one or more primitive vertices, *i.e.* vertices in which no edge ends.[1]

A neighbourhood of a point p is the set of all points q which can be connected with p by a path $pp'p'' \ldots p^{(n)} = q$ where the edges pp', $p'p''$, $\ldots$, $p^{(n-1)} p^{(n)}$ belong to the tree. Thus an open set has the property that with every point p it contains all points q which can be connected with p by a path.

The following remark, due in principle to Weyl [244], shows the intuitive origin of the topological interpretation. Let us consider sentences of the form $x \in X$ where X is a subset of V. Each such sentence can be either true or false. Let us call it strongly true (or strongly false) if it remains true (false) for all points x' lying sufficiently close to x. Thus the sentence $x \in X$ is strongly true if x lies in the interior of X and strongly false if it lies in the interior of $V-X$. For an x lying on the boundary of X (*i.e.* in the set $\bar{X} \cap \overline{V - X}$ where the bar denotes closure) the sentence is neither strongly true nor strongly false. All this is in accordance with the intuitionistic conception of a set according to which a finite amount of information concerning x should be sufficient to decide whether x belongs or does not belong to the set. Of course this remark, while indicating the connection between topology and the intuitionistic logic, does not by itself suffice to explain the success of Tarski's construction.

Formally speaking Tarski's result says that open subsets of a topological space V form a matrix in which all intuitionistically provable formulae are valid; for a suitable V (*e.g.* if V is a Euclidean

---

[1] Formally speaking, a tree is the graph of a one-many relation R such that the relation xR^nx holds for no x and no integer n.

plane) this matrix is adequate for the intuitionistic logic. Of course
the general notion of a matrix was known long before Tarski's work
on the intuitionistic logic; but never before his work had a matrix
with so many elements been actually used nor had any one considered matrices having the structure of a topological space.

Several later studies of the intuitionistic logic and of other many-
valued systems drew their inspiration from Tarski's paper.

We add some further remarks on the proof of Tarski's result. In
one direction it is very easy: it is a routine matter to check that the
axioms (A), (K), (I), (F) are valid in matrices consisting of open
subsets of an arbitrary topological space V and that the rule of
modus ponens preserves validity in this matrix. Thus all intuitionistic
theorems are valid in these matrices. It is much more difficult to
show that exactly those formulae are valid in the matrix that are
intuitionistically provable (provided that V satisfies certain conditions). In order to obtain this result Tarski used the following result
of Jaśkowski [85]: There exists a denumerable sequence of finite
matrices M_n such that a propositional formula A is intuitionistically
provable if and only if it is valid in at least one of these matrices.

It is not difficult to describe Jaśkowski's matrices. Each of them
consists of open subsets of a finite space determined by a tree. The
first matrix corresponds to a tree with but one vertex, and the subsequent ones are obtained from the preceeding ones by two operations
which we call O' and O''. The operation O' is simply the operation of
joining trees together (without adding new edges to any of them);
O'' consists of joining to each other two trees T_1, T_2 so as to add to
them one vertex which is joined by edges to the primitive vertices
of T_1 and of T_2. This is illustrated by diagram 3.

This clear description of Jaśkowski's matrices is due to Grzegorczyk [70]; proofs of Jaśkowski's theorem are contained in Rose
[186] and Scott [197].

Subsequent development brought essential simplifications to

Diagram 3.

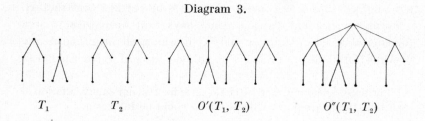

T_1 T_2 $O'(T_1, T_2)$ $O''(T_1, T_2)$

Tarski's original proof; see McKinsey and Tarski [142]. Instead of Jaśkowski's matrices Tarski used certain other matrices whose elements are formulae. The idea of using such matrices goes back to Lindenbaum.

The intuitionistic logic is but one of many non-classical logics. Several other such "logics" were defined first by Łukasiewicz and Post and later by other logicians. Some of them were invented for purely formal reason, but several others, *e.g.* modal logic, possess intrinsic philosophical value. It seems to us that the intuitionistic logic occupies a privileged position among these systems: it is the only logic, so far constructed which is actually being used by a relatively large group of actively working scientists. It is also the only one which has been extended beyond propositional logic and the logic of quantifiers and used in the development of certain parts of mathematics. Łukasiewicz, who was the first to conceive an idea of a logic different from the usual one, hoped that one day several logics will emerge which will actually be used, as are for instance the non-Euclidean geometries. Most of the non-classical logics invented so far are not being actually used although several of them are being studied in the meta-mathematical fashion on the basis of the two-valued logic. It looks as if the intuitionistic logic were the only one in the case of which Łukasiewicz's plan has still some chance of realization. At the same time this logic is based on an original and internally coherent view of mathematics. These two circumstances explain the vivid interest which the intuitionistic logic has raised from the moment it was created.

Lecture II

The incompleteness of arithmetic

In this lecture we shall be concerned with another important contribution of the early thirties to the study of the foundations of mathematics, especially with the so called first incompleteness theorem of Gödel [54] which states that the usual axiomatic systems of arithmetic of integers are incomplete. In order to explain the importance of this result we insert some brief historical comments.

Since the publication of the works of Frege and of Russell and Whitehead logicians believed that each intuitively correct deduction can be reconstructed in the classical logical calculus. It was also believed that by adding suitable axioms to the logical calculus we shall be able to construct axiomatic systems in which every intuitively correct mathematical statement will be provable. If there were doubts as to how the axioms (*e.g.* the axioms for set theory) are to be chosen, nobody (except the intuitionists) felt the slightest doubt that the axioms of Peano fully describe the notion of an integer. Hence it was generally believed that all intuitively correct statements of arithmetic are formally derivable from these axioms. This belief was the basis of the philosophical views of the Hilbert school. The representatives of this school were convinced that the notion of truth (the truth of an arithmetical statement) has been defined, since true statements coincide with statements formally derivable from the axioms of Peano. They shifted therefore the emphasis from the problem of defining truth (which was always considered the central problem of philosophy) to the more formal problem of establishing the consistency of Peano's axioms by using very simple combinatorial arguments. We remark parenthetically that such a proof, if it existed, would be interesting independently of the question whether intuitive arithmetic is reducible to Peano's axioms.

Gödel's discovery showed, first, that the identification of true formulae with formulae formally derivable from Peano's axioms is

untenable. Secondly, he showed that a consistency proof as required
by Hilbert does not exist unless arithmetic is inconsistent. Thus the
whole program of the formalist school was dealt a blow from which
this school has never really recovered.

Gödel's work became quickly famous. Since it is generally known
we can limit our exposition to brief indications.

The main tool invented by Gödel and used by him in the proofs
of his theorems was the so-called arithmetization of meta-mathematics. It consists simply of an enumeration of formulae and sequences of formulae with the help of integers. (We shall call the integer correlated with a formula, or a sequence of formulae, under this
enumeration the number of this formula or sequence.) The existence
of such an enumeration is secured by the fact that the set of all
formulae has the same power as the set of integers. Because of this
fact we can correlate with each set of formulae and each relation
between formulae a set or a relation between integers. In a system
in which arithmetical theorems can be proved we can also prove
theorems equivalent to certain theorems about formulae. In this
way it is theoretically possible to construct within arithmetic
statements referring to themselves. Self-referential statements used
carelessly can lead to inconsistencies, known as semantic antinomies.
Well known examples of these antinomies are the paradox of the
liar and Richard's paradox. Gödel's first theorem amounts to showing
that these paradoxes would indeed be present in the axiomatic
arithmetic if this system were complete. As shown by Wang [242],
each of the semantic antinomies known so far can be transformed
into an incompleteness proof.

In order to describe Gödel's proof we need some meta-mathematical definitions. Let us assume that T is a consistent system of
arithmetic among whose expressions there are the symbols $\bar{0}, \bar{1}, \bar{2}, \ldots$,
called numerals. Let us assume that to each integer n there is associated a numeral $\bar{n}$ and that the formula $\bar{m} \neq \bar{n}$ is provable in T whenever m and n are different integers.

We shall say that a formula F with one free variable is a weak
description of a set X of integers if for any integer n the formula
$F(\bar{n})$ is provable in T just in case n is an element of X. Sets which
possess at least one weak description in T are called weakly representable in T. There are only denumerably many such sets because
the number of different formulae is denumerable. If F is a weak
description of X and $\neg F$ is a weak description of the complement $-X$

of X, then we call F a strong description of X in T; sets X which have at least one strong description in T are called strongly representable in T.

Weak and strong representability are two of the many possible ways of making precise the vague notion of expressibility of an intuitively given property within a formal system. Consider *e.g.* the set $X = \{0, 2, 4, \ldots\}$ of even numbers; its elements are the integers possessing the intuitively clear property of being divisible by 2. We express this property in the axiomatic arithmetic T by the formula $F(y) = \bigvee_x [y = x + x]$. Obviously $F(\bar{n})$ is provable in T if $n \in X$ and $\neg F(\bar{n})$ is provable in X if it is not the case that $n \in X$; assuming that T is consistent we can say that X is strongly representable in T. It is much more difficult to give an example of a set which is weakly but not strongly representable in a system T. In fact, the existence of an example of this kind implies the incompleteness of T: for if T is complete and F is a weak description of X in T, then $n \,\bar{\in}\, X$ holds just in case when $F(\bar{n})$ is not provable in T, *i.e.* when $\neg F(\bar{n})$ is provable in T and hence $\neg F$ is a weak description of $-X$.

In an analogous way we define the weak and strong representability of a set consisting of pairs or triples or quadruples of integers. Thus we can speak of the representability of binary, ternary, quaternary *etc.* relations between integers. We can also define the representability of functions. *E.g.* if f is a function of one argument ranging over integers whose values are also integers, then we say that a formula $F(x, y)$ with two free variables represents f if (*i*) F weakly represents the relation $f(n) = m$; (*ii*) the formula $\bigwedge_x \bigvee_y! \, F(x,y)$ is provable in T. There is no need to distinguish in this case between weak and strong representability.

One can show that if certain formulae which we shall not specify here are provable in T, then there is a set U strongly representable in T which consists of triples of integers and which is "universal" in the following sense: whenever a set X of integers is weakly representable in T, there is an integer e such that

(1) $\qquad\qquad n \in X \equiv \bigvee_p [<e, p, n> \in U].$

U is simply the set of triples $<x, y, z>$ such that x is a number of a formula F with one free variable, and y the number of a finite sequence of formulae whose last term is $F(\bar{z})$ and which represents the formal proof of its last term in T. It is of course not obvious that such a set U is strongly representable; at least half of Gödel's paper was devoted to a proof that this is really so.

Another important lemma is the following theorem on projections: under suitable assumptions concerning T it is the case that if X is a set of pairs which is strongly representable in T, then the set $\left\{ x : \bigvee\limits_{y} (<x, y> \in X) \right\}$ is weakly representable.

The theorems on the existence of a universal set and on projections allow us to prove very quickly that T is incomplete. The set $X = \left\{ n : \bigwedge\limits_{q} (< n, q, n > \bar{\in} U) \right\}$ is easily shown not to be weakly representable; otherwise there would be an integer e for which (1) is true and hence we would obtain

$$\bigwedge_{q} [<n, q, n> \bar{\in} U] \equiv \bigvee_{p} [<e, p, n> \in U]$$

whence for $n = e$

$$\bigwedge_{q} [<e, q, e> \bar{\in} U] \equiv \bigvee_{p} [<e, p, e> \in U]$$

which is a contradiction.

On the other hand the complement of X is weakly representable according to the theorem on projections. Hence there exist sets which are weakly but not strongly representable, which implies (as we remarked above) the incompleteness of T.

We will now discuss the assumptions which have to be made in order to prove the theorem on projections.

Let X be a set of pairs of integers weakly represented by a formula F. It is natural to expect that the set $P = \left\{ x : \bigvee\limits_{y} [<x, y> \in X] \right\}$ will be represented by the formula $\bigvee\limits_{w} F(u, w)$. This is indeed the case under certain conditions. Let us first assume that $<x, y> \in X$, i.e. that $F(\bar{x}, \bar{y})$ is provable. Using a well-known law of logic we obtain that the formula $\bigvee\limits_{w} F(\bar{x}, w)$ is provable. The only assumption needed in this step is that to every integer y there exists a corresponding numeral. If, as it is often admitted, numerals consist of symbols "1" placed one after another, then our assumption states that the length of each numeral is an integer and that for each integer there exists a numeral of this length. Now let us assume that x is not in the set P, *i.e.* that for every y the pair $<x, y>$ is not in X. Hence — in view of the strong representability of X — we obtain that for every y the formula $\neg F(\bar{x}, \bar{y})$ is provable in **T**. In order to infer that the formula $\bigvee_{w} F(\bar{x}, w)$ is not provable in **T** Gödel assumed that whenever all formulae of the infinite sequence $\neg A(\bar{0})$, $\neg A(\bar{1}), \ldots$ are provable in **T** then the existential statement $\bigvee_{y} A(y)$ is not provable in **T**. This assumption is called the ω-consistency of **T**.

The theorem on the universal set requires that certain formulae which we shall not enumerate here be provable in **T**.

Altogether we have 3 assumptions: (A) the one-one correspondence between numerals and integers, (B) the ω-consistency of **T**, (C) the provability in **T** of certain formulae.

Assumptions (B) and (C) were discussed almost from the beginning of the whole theory. Rosser showed in an important paper [187] that one can replace the assumption of ω-consistency by the much simpler assumption of consistency. The proof of the theorem on projections must then be modified in that a more sophisticated formula must be used to show the weak representability of the set P. It follows from his proof that each consistent extension of Peano's arithmetic is incomplete provided that the set of the numbers of its axioms is weakly representable. Consistent theories with this property are called after Tarski [231] essentially incomplete. We shall see later the importance of these theories for the problem known as the decision problem. Especially important is the fact that there exist essentially incomplete theories based on a finite number of axioms. The simplest such theory (Vaught, unpublished) has one primitive notion R which denotes a binary relation and is based on the axioms

$$\bigvee_{x} \bigwedge_{y} \neg (yRx), \qquad \bigwedge_{xy} \bigvee_{z} \bigwedge_{t} \left\{ tRz \equiv [(t = x) \vee tRy] \right\}.$$

The assumption (C) can be modified in various ways but of course cannot be dropped altogether. The assumption (A) was noted not long ago by Rieger. Let us discuss it a little more closely. The majority of mathematicians believe that the notion of an integer is uniquely determined and that the integers form a well determined set. If one adheres to this view, then it is obvious that the lengths of formulae are integers and that the assumption (A) is satisfied. It is possible, however, to take a different standpoint and to insist that each set of objects satisfying Peano's axioms can be taken as the set of integers. It is known that there exist many mutually non-isomorphic models of Peano's axioms; hence one can assume that one such set is used in intuitive mathematics and another is used to count symbols in formulae. Then the assumption (A) need not be satisfied. In Rieger's view this remark invalidates the philosophical claims of Gödel's discovery; it is more appropriate to say that it merely discloses one of the assumptions on which Gödel's theorem rests.

Our discussion has so far been limited to one of the many results contained in Gödel's paper [54]. We shall now review briefly its second main result. It is appropriate to remark that Gödel's paper was exceptionally rich in new ideas and that only now, after more than 30 years, the wealth of problems stemming directly from it begins to show signs of exhaustion.

Gödel's second main result is his second undecidability theorem. It was merely sketched in the published paper and was due to appear with a detailed proof in the second part of his paper. This second part was never written, however.

Let Z be the set of pairs $<x, y>$ such that y is the number of a formula of formalized arithmetic $\boldsymbol{T}$ and x the number of its formal proof in $\boldsymbol{T}$. It was shown by Gödel that Z is strongly representable in $\boldsymbol{T}$; his proof indicated how to construct a formula F which strongly represents Z in $\boldsymbol{T}$. Let k be the number of the formula $0 \neq 0$ or of any other formula which is refutable in $\boldsymbol{T}$. The formula $\bigwedge_x [\neg F(x, \bar{k})]$ was denoted by Gödel by Wid. Its intuitive content is: there is no formal proof in $\boldsymbol{T}$ of the formula $0 \neq 0$.

The second undecidability theorem asserts that the formula Wid is not provable in $\boldsymbol{T}$ provided that $\boldsymbol{T}$ is consistent. If we assume that every combinatorial proof can be formalized within arithmetic, then Gödel's second theorem shows that Hilbert's program of proving in a purely combinatorial way the consistency of arithmetic is not realizable. This assumption is open for discussion, however, as we shall see later when we discuss Gentzen's theorem. Another objection which can be raised against such interpretation of Gödel's second undecidability theorem is this: There are many formulae F strongly representing Z in $\boldsymbol{T}$; Gödel's theorem is valid only for some such formulae. It is not immediately obvious why the theorem proved for just this formula should have a philosophical importance while a similar theorem obtained by a different choice of a formula strongly representing the same set Z is simply false.

Let us consider as an example the formula $F'(x, y) : F(x, y) \wedge \neg F(x, \bar{k})$. If T is consistent, then F' strongly represents Z in T just as F does. Thus the formula $Wid' = \bigwedge_x \neg F'(x, \bar{k})$ can be considered as another formal expression of the consistency of T. However, Wid' is obviously provable in T.

The reason why the second undecidability theorem holds for some formulae strongly representing Z but fails for others is this: the main step in the proof of this theorem consists of a formalization of an intuitively correct deduction in T. (We may add parenthetically that this deduction happens to be the proof of Gödel's first theorem but that this is not essential for the explanation of the phenomenon just described.) The intuitive deduction uses not only premisses of the form $<x, y> \epsilon Z$ and $<x, y> \bar{\epsilon} Z$ for some particular integers x, y but also some properties of Z expressible as general statements. When we formalize the deduction in T we can express the premisses $<x, y> \epsilon Z$, $<x, y> \bar{\epsilon} Z$ by the formulae $F(\bar{x}, \bar{y})$, $\neg F(\bar{x}, \bar{y})$ which are provable in T for all formulae F strongly representing Z. This is no more true for the general statements; for some formulae strongly representing Z these general statements may turn out to be provable in T and for the others not provable.

The first analysis of the second undecidability theorem from this point of view was given by Bernays in [81]. The conditions he imposed on F pertained to the provability of certain general statements in which F (and other related formulae) occur.

A deeper analysis was undertaken by Feferman [36] who introduced the notions of a recursive formula and of a recursively enumerable formula. In order to describe his construction let us assume that ζ is a function taking on values 0 or 1 according as $<x, y> \epsilon Z$ or $<x, y> \bar{\epsilon} Z$. Gödel showed that ζ can be obtained by consecutive substitutions from the function $x + 1$ and a finite number of auxiliary functions τ_j which are defined recursively, *i.e.* which satisfy equations of the form

$$(*) \qquad \tau_j (0, x) = \alpha (x), \qquad \tau_j (n + 1, x) = \beta (\tau_j(n, x), n, x)$$

where β and α involve only the functions $\tau_0, \ldots, \tau_{j-1}$.

If we adjoin to T symbols $\bar{\tau}_j$ for the functions τ_j and add the formulae (*) as new axioms, then we obtain a system which we shall call a primitive recursive extension of T. Now a formula F is called primitive recursive if there is a primitive recursive extension

T' of T in which the equivalence $F(x, y) \equiv (\bar{\zeta}(x, y) = 0)$ is provable
($\bar{\zeta}$ is the symbol for the combination of symbols $\bar{\tau}_j$ corresponding
to the function ζ). It is easy to show that such a formula F strongly
represents Z in T. It can also be shown (as was already done in
effect by Gödel in [54]) that for every strongly representable set Y
there is a primitive recursive formula strongly representing it.

A formula obtained from a primitive recursive formula by prefix-
ing a string of existential quantifiers to it is called recursively enumerable. Feferman's main result states that if T is consistent and F is
a recursively enumerable formula strongly representing Z, then the
formula $\bigwedge_{x} \neg F(x, \bar{k})$ is not provable in T. The theorem is valid not
only for the formal arithmetic based on Peano's axioms but for an
arbitrary extension of this system.

The general problem brought up by this analysis can be described
as follows: there is given, on the one hand, a set X of integers (or of
pairs, triples *etc.*) and, on the other hand, a formal language. We
are looking for the best possible definition of X in T, *i.e.* for a definition which makes, of all the intuitively true formulae involving X,
as many as possible provable in T. If we use as definitions formulae
strongly representing X, then we can prove in T every formula
corresponding to the statements $n \in X$ or $n \bar{\in} X$. If we use primitive
recursive formulae as definitions of X we can prove more true statements and still more such statements become provable if we use
recursively enumerable formulae. But it is easy to show that no
formal definition of the set Z used above will make all *general* arithmetical statements provable in arithmetic. This follows simply from
the remark due to Rosser [187] that the set

$$\left\{ p : \bigwedge_{x} [(<x, p> \bar{\in} Z) \wedge (<x, neg(p)> \bar{\in} Z)] \right\}$$

is not recursively enumerable (*neg* is here a function such that whenever p is the number of a formula, $neg(p)$ is the number of its negation).

Let us now return to Gödel's second undecidability theorem. For
reasons which were set forth above we do not think that this theorem
overthrew Hilbert's program although it doubtless showed a weakness
in its original formulation. But quite apart from this philosophical
claim, Gödel's theorem proved to be a very powerful tool in investig-
ating the relative strength of various axiomatic systems. Whenever
we have two systems, both of which contain arithmetic, so that we

can prove in one of them the formula *Wid* expressing the consistency of the other, then there is no possibility of interpreting the first system in the second. Such applications were made *e.g.* by Kemeny [93] who compared the relative strength of Russell's theory of types and of Zermelo's axiomatic set theory. Further applications were found by Feferman [37].

In addition to the two undecidability theorems Gödel's paper contained various other results which we shall discuss in the lecture dealing with decision problems. It also contained some deep remarks concerning the way in which the adjunction of variables of higher types modifies the set of provable arithmetical formulae. These remarks were understood only long after the publication of the paper.

As we saw above, Gödel's paper was devoted mainly to problems of consistency and completeness of formal systems. The method invented by Gödel was to compare intuitively true properties of mathematical objects with properties expressible in the formal system under consideration. The sharp division of reasoning into intuitive meta-mathematics and formal mathematics was rejected on principle by the intuitionists; in the hands of Gödel this very division turned out to be an extremely valuable tool for establishing properties of formal systems. This brings once more to light the deep differences between the approach to foundational problems of the intuitionistic school and the approach of the more conservative meta-mathematical school of Hilbert.

Lecture III

Semantics

We shall call the study of relations between mathematical objects and formal expressions naming them "logical semantics". This description of logical semantics is not essentially different from the description of semantics given in linguistics although linguists would not limit themselves to mathematical objects but would replace them by any objects whatsoever and would also replace expressions of a formal language by sentences of the everyday language. Tarski was the first to realize that the basic ideas of semantics can be applied to the study of formalized languages.

When developing semantics we must carefully distinguish between the language in which we speak (the "syntax-language" or the "meta-language") and the language about which we speak (the "object-language"). The meaning of expressions of a language cannot be described in the same language. Thus we have in semantics the same pair of languages which we encountered in our discussion of Gödel's incompleteness theorem. There is a deep difference, however, between the way Tarski developed semantics and the way Gödel discussed certain relations between formulae and sets of integers. Gödel was interested only in very special relations of this kind and tried in every case to reduce these relations to ones which could (via his numbering) be expressed in arithmetic. Tarski on the contrary aims at a general theory of semantic relations; he notes that in some cases these relations are essentially reducible to arithmetic but considers this as a secondary phenomenon. His meta-languages are always very rich and contain sizable parts of set theory.

Tarski showed that all semantic notions can be reduced to one fundamental notion, *viz.* that of a value of a formula. Taken by itself a formula is just a string of symbols and is devoid of any meaning. Thus in order to define the value of a formula we must first fix the values of the simple symbols out of which it is constructed. We shall limit ourselves to the case of first-order formulae, *i.e.* formulae which are constructed from individual variables, predicates, propositional connectives and quantifiers.

It is customary to assume that the propositional connectives denote Boolean operations in a two-element algebra $\{\mathfrak{B}, \mathfrak{F}\}$ whose elements may be called the truth-values. We need, furthermore, three things: (a) an interpretation of the variables; we assume that they denote elements of a set A; (b) an interpretation of predicates; we assume that a predicate with p arguments denotes a relation with p arguments ranging over A, *i.e.* a function which correlates a truth-value with every p-tuple of the elements of A; (c) an interpretation of quantifiers; we assume that the general quantifier denotes a function Q from subsets of A to the set $\{\mathfrak{B}, \mathfrak{F}\}$ such that $Q(A) = \mathfrak{B}$ and $Q(X) = \mathfrak{F}$ for all the other values of X; the interpretation of the existential quantifier is defined by duality.

These conventions determine the interpretation of the language. Since the interpretation of the connectives is the same in all models and the interpretation of quantifiers depends but on A, we see that a model is completely determined by A and by the relations correlated with the predicates.

Once a model M is fixed we can define by induction the value of a formula in M for a given assignment of elements of A to the free variables occurring in the formula. The definition proceeds by induction. The value of an atomic formula $P(x_1, \ldots, x_p)$ is equal to the value of the relation associated with P for the arguments $a_1, \ldots, a_p$ correlated with the variables $x_1, \ldots, x_p$. The value of $F \vee G$ is the Boolean sum of the values of F and of G; and similarly for other connectives. The value of $\bigwedge_{x_i} F$ for a given assignment π of the elements of A to the free variables of $\bigwedge_{x_i} F$ is equal to $Q(X)$ where X is the set of all a in A with the following property: the value of F for an assignment which correlates a with x_i and is otherwise identical with the assignment π is $\mathfrak{B}$.

In what follows we shall use the customary notation $\models_M F[a, b, \ldots]$ for the relation defined by the following requirement: the value of F in M for the assignment correlating the elements $a, b, \ldots$ with the consecutive free variables of F is $\mathfrak{B}$. This relation is also read: $a, b, \ldots$ satisfy F in M.

The inductive definition of the value of a formula was for the first time formulated explicitly by Tarski, but the notion itself was well understood intuitively and used successfully long before Tarski's paper. Hilbert and his students constantly used the notions of general validity and of satisfiability of formulae which are essentially equivalent to the notion defined by Tarski.

We do not think it essential that Tarski formulated his definition not for a first-order language but for other more comprehensive languages. I am inclined to think that this was on the contrary a somewhat unfortunate circumstance which clouded rather than clarified the problem. From the point of view of syntax there is no essential difference between languages of the first and (say) of the second-order. The language of the second-order can be treated as the language of the first-order with the stipulation that we use special letters for certain variables and place them in a special way in the formulae. What essentially counts is the interpretation (or a model) of the language. Tarski in his first paper chose an interpretation under which the values of second-order variables were arbitrary subsets of A. This is not the only possible model, however, as was shown later by Henkin [77] (*cf.* also Mostowski [149]).

These remarks should not be interpreted as an indication of any doubts about the importance of the progress due to the introduction of semantic notions. Semantics brought order into the various parts of meta-mathematics and allowed one to define and discuss several natural and important notions. While the notions of semantics are extremely simple and natural, the problem of their formalization turned out to be rather deep; it has lead to several new discoveries. Let us discuss these two applications of semantics in turn.

The best known and at the same time the most important notion of semantics is that of logical consequence. Let $F, A_1, \ldots, A_n$ be formulae of the language under consideration. We say then that F is a logical consequence of $A_1, \ldots, A_n$ if, for every model and for every assignment of values to the free variables of these formulae, it is the case that whenever the value of $A_1, \ldots, A_n$ is $\mathfrak{B}$, then so is the value of F. For a first-order language this notion coincides with that of deducibility by means of suitable formal rules of proof. Its advantage as compared with the latter notion lies in its wider range of application. For instance, there exist no adequate rules of proof for higher order languages, and hence the semantic notion of consequence is the only one which we can use in connection with such languages.

Another important notion is that of definability in a given model ***M***.

We say that a is definable in M if there is a formula F with one free variable such that a is the unique element x of A for which $\models_M F[x]$. A set X of elements of A is definable in M if there is a formula F with one free variable such that for every a in A the equivalence $a \in X \equiv \models_M F[a]$ holds. Similar definitions can be formulated for relations with an arbitrary number of arguments.

An interesting and not yet completely solved problem is the following: Is the set of elements definable in a model M itself definable in this model? The answer obviously depends on the model. Tarski investigated this problem for the standard models of higher order arithmetics and found that the set of definable families of sets of integers is not definable. For the set of definable sets of integers, however, the problem has recently been solved by J. W. Addison with the use of the notion of forcing due to Cohen (cf. lecture XV).

The notion of definability in a model should not be confused with a completely different but similarly named notion of definability in a theory. This latter notion is not semantic but syntactic in character. Let us explain this for the case of definability of sets. Consider an axiomatic theory T with the primitive notions $R_1, \ldots, R_k$, Y and based on certain axioms. We assume that Y has just one argument. Tarski [223] says that Y is definable in T in terms of $R_1, \ldots, R_k$ if there is a formula F not involving Y which has one free variable and is such that the equivalence $Y(x) \equiv F(x)$ is provable in T.

If Y is definable in T in terms of $R_1, \ldots, R_k$ and if all the axioms of T are true in a model M, then the set X which interprets Y in M is definable in M and the defining formula can be chosen so that Y does not occur in it. The converse theorem is not true, however; one can easily give trivial examples of theories whose primitive notions R, Y have the following properties: (i) Y is not definable in terms of R in T; (ii) in every model M in which all the axioms of T are true the interpretation of Y is definable in M by a formula not involving Y.

We shall now discuss the properties of the following function: the value of F in M. For simplicity's sake we shall assume that no free variables occur in F. We shall also assume that among the relations of the model M there are the following arithmetical relations: x is an integer, $x = y + z$, $x = yz$. It is then possible (using the Gödelian machinery of numbering of formulae) to replace the value-relation (the value of F in M is $\mathfrak{B}$) by the arithmetical relation

(*) f is the number of a formula without free variables which is true in M.

Tarski asked the following questions:

(1) Is the relation (*) definable in M?

(2) If (*) is not definable in M, what new relations should we add to M in order to ensure the definability of (*) in the extended model?

The famous theorem due to Tarski and named after him states that the answer to question (1) is indeed negative. The proof is obtained by a simple application of the diagonal procedure.

Let us enumerate all formulae with one free variable x and denote by F_n the n-th formula; let $D_k(x)$ be a formula which defines k in M (its existence follows easily from the assumption that M contains the basic arithmetical relations). Put $Z_n = \left\{ k : \models_M \bigvee_x [F_n(x) \wedge D_k(x)] \right\}$; by a diagonal argument the set $Z = \left\{ n : n \,\bar{\epsilon}\, Z_n \right\}$ is different from all sets Z_n. We shall now derive a contradiction from the assumption that (*) is definable in M by showing that if (*) were definable in M by a formula G, then Z would be equal to one of the sets Z_q.

The Gödel number of $\bigvee_x [F_n(x) \wedge D_n(x)]$ is a function of n; it can be shown that this function is definable. Let S be a defining formula. Hence, for every n,

$$\models_M \bigvee_{x,\,y} [D_n(x) \wedge S(x, y) \wedge \neg G(y)] \text{ if and only if not}$$
$$\models_M \bigvee_x [F_n(x) \wedge D_n(x)],$$

i.e.

$$\models_M \bigvee_x [D_n(x) \wedge F_q(x)] \text{ if and only if not } \models_M \bigvee_x [F_n(x) \wedge D_n(x)]$$

where q is the number of the formula $\bigvee_y [S(x, y) \wedge \neg G(y)]$. Replacing here n by q we obtain a contradiction.

Tarski's theorem applied to Peano's arithmetic yields at once the incompleteness theorem. Indeed the set of (numbers of) formulae derivable from Peano's axioms is easily shown to be definable in the (standard) model of arithmetic whereas Tarski's theorem shows that the set of formulae true in this model is not definable in it. Hence the two sets are different which is — in essence — the contention of the incompleteness theorem.

The solution of problem (2) is of course not uniquely determined.

We can obviously add various relations to the model M in such a way that the relation (*) be definable in the new model. The most natural solution is to add to M the relations expressed by "a is a finite sequence of elements of M" and "the elements of a sequence a satisfy in M the formula with the number x (*i.e.* the value of this formula is $\mathfrak{B}$)". We shall denote this extended model by M'.

The second of these relations can be defined by induction, but it is an induction of a very peculiar form. The usual inductive definition of a function has the form

$$f(0, a) = p(x), \qquad f(n + 1, a) = q(f(n, a), n, a)$$

where p and q are given functions. The relation of satisfaction can be defined only by a much more complicated scheme of induction in which the value of $f(n + 1, a)$ depends on the values $f(s, b)$ where $s \leq n$ and b is arbitrary. Thus the second inductive equation has the form

$$f(n + 1, a) = \Phi \left((\lambda s)_{s \leq n} (\lambda b) f(s, b), n, a \right)$$

where $(\lambda s)_{s \leq n} (\lambda b) f(s, b)$ is the function which is defined for $s \leq n$ and for an arbitrary b and whose value is $f(s, b)$, and where Φ is a functional whose values are integers, whose first argument is a function and whose remaining arguments are integers.

In this way Tarski's theory ties up with the theory of inductive definitions and allows us to establish a theorem saying that there exist types of inductive definitions which cannot be reduced to the ordinary inductive definitions in a purely arithmetical way.

Let us finally discuss the problem whether it is possible to develop an axiomatic theory of semantics.

Tarski showed that for any axiomatized theory T we can set up an axiomatic theory T' embodying certain features of the semantics of T. The primitive notions of T' are, in addition to those of T, the following: the notions of arithmetic (which allow us to speak in T' of numbers correlated with formulae of T); the set of all finite sequences of the elements of the universe of T; and the satisfaction relation.

The axioms of T' include those of T; there are, furthermore axioms corresponding to the inductive clauses of the definition of the satisfaction relation, and axioms characterizing the notion of a finite sequence.

If *M* is a model of *T* in which all axioms of *T* are true and if *M'* is the extension of *M* defined above, then all the axioms of *T'* are true in *M'*. If *T* is based on a finite number of axioms (or if a suitable form of the rule of mathematical induction is valid in *T'*), then the consistency of *T* is provable in *T'*. Thus *T'* is a theory which is essentially stronger than *T* (*cf.* p. 26). The method of proving the consistency of a given theory *T* in a stronger theory is often accomplished by interpreting *T'* in this stronger theory.

An interesting further relationship between *T* and *T'* is formulated in a theorem going back to Gödel [58] and developed further by Kreisel and Wang [117]: There exist infinitely many formulae of *T* which are provable in *T* (and hence in *T'*) but whose shortest proof in *T* is k times longer than its shortest proof in *T'*. Here k can be any integer fixed in advance. Thus *T'* is stronger than *T* also in the sense that many proofs already existing in *T* can be essentially shortened in *T'*. Proof of this theorem also uses ideas of semantics but is too involved to be given here.

We thus see that the development of semantics not only allowed one to make precise various intuitively clear meta-mathematical notions but also threw new light on the problems of incompleteness. Semantic ideas simplify Gödel's argument and complement his theorem by showing that axiomatic theories containing arithmetic are not capable of defining their own satisfaction relation nor defining certain other semantic notions. Thus semantics turned out to be useful both in the "constructive" as in the "destructive" parts of meta-mathematical study.

Lecture IV

Computable functions

The need of a systematic study of functions whose values can be calculated by a finite process was felt already in the Hilbert school. Hilbert and his students devoted much attention to the problem known as the decision problem for the first-order logic, *i.e.* to the problem of finding a method which would allow one to decide in a finite number of steps whether any given formula is or is not provable. Many similar problems can be formulated in logic as well as in mathematics. To mention only a few, we have *e.g.* the problem of deciding whether a given string of symbols is a correctly built logical formula, whether a given arithmetical formula is decidable in Peano's arithmetic, whether a given polynomial with integral coefficients is irreducible, *etc*. In each of these examples we have a denumerable class C of objects (formulae, strings of symbols, polynomials) and a subclass C' of this class (the class of provable formulae, of well formed formulae, of irreducible polynomials). We may define a function f on C by putting $f(x) = 0$ for $x \in C'$ and $f(x) = 1$ for $x \in C - C'$ (the characteristic function of C'). The problem is then to find a method allowing us to calculate f in a finite number of steps or to prove that such a method does not exist.

We can obviously solve various problems of this kind without knowing the general definition of a finitistic method. Mathematicians certainly did not feel the need of formulating such a definition when they gave irreducibility criteria for polynomials with integral coefficients. The situation is of course different if we want to show that a specific problem does not admit an algorithmic solution.

Since the class C dealt with in the decision problem is usually denumerable, we can limit ourselves to the case when C is a set of integers. The characteristic function f of C' is then an arithmetical function (*i.e.* a function whose arguments and values are integers), and our problem is to define a class of arithmetical functions whose values can be found in a finitistic way. We are discussing this problem right after the general account of semantics and of the incompleteness theorem partly for historical reasons and partly because there is a far-reaching analogy between the notion of a computable function and the notion of a function definable in a given model. However much we would like to "mathematize" the definition of computability, we can never get completely rid of the semantic aspect of this concept. The process of computation is a linguistic notion (presupposing that our notion of a language is sufficiently general); what we have to do is to delimit a class of those functions (considered as abstract mathematical objects) for which there exists a corresponding linguistic object (a process of computation). In the case of the notion of definability we also encountered the situation that we tried to define a class of functions (or sets or relations) for which there exist certain linguistic objects (formal definitions in the model).

Historically the first example of a class of computable functions was furnished by the primitive recursive functions. They can be defined as the functions that can be obtained from constants and from the successor function $x + 1$ by means of substitutions, of the identification of arguments, of adding superfluous arguments and of applying the schema of primitive recursion (*cf.* p. 32)

$$(*) \qquad f(0, a) = p(a), \qquad f(n + 1, a) = q(f(n, a), n, a).$$

This class became very famous after Gödel showed that these functions suffice for the purpose of numbering all formulae and all sequences of formulae. It is obvious, however, that the class of primitive recursive functions does not include all computable functions. This follows from the existence of a computable function which is universal for the class of the primitive recursive function. A universal function is a function of two variables U such that for every n the function $f(x) = U(n, x)$ is primitive recursive and that each primitive recursive function can be so obtained. Obviously the "diagonal" function $U(n, n) + 1$ is not primitive recursive. It is slightly more cumbersome to prove that U is a computable function. Without going into details we can say that n is a code number which indicates the order of the operations of substitutions and recursions which are used to define a given function as well as the order of the starting functions. Thus $U(n, x)$ is the value at the point x of the function obtained from the starting functions by the use of process with the code number n.

It can be shown similarly that various extensions of the class of primitive recursive functions which are obtained by using a schema of recursion more general than (*) do not exhaust the set of computable functions. This latter class must obviously have the property that no universal function for this class is itself contained in the class.

Several definitions of computable functions and sets were proposed in the decade 1930—1940 and still others appeared later. It is significant that all these definitions, though formally different, proved to be equivalent. We shall not enter into details of these definitions but only give general indications.

1. *Definitions using the notion of representability.* These definitions were among the first to be proposed. The first author who proposed to identify computable functions and sets with the ones which are representable in a formal system was Church [16]. Further definitions of a similar character were proposed by Herbrand and Gödel [57] and by Gödel alone [58]. Church used a very special system called the calculus of λ-conversion, Gödel and Herbrand a weak system whose expressions are exclusively identities. More general was the approach of Gödel in [58]; he noted there that the class of functions which are representable in the formal system of arithmetic of the k-th order is independent of k. This observation was put in a general form by Bernays in [81]; it was shown there that the class of functions representable in any formal system satisfying some very general conditions is one and the same. The main condition to be satisfied is that the relation expressed by: "m is the number of a proof of a formula number n" is primitive recursive.

2. *Arithmetical definitions.* For any relation between integers $R(x, y_1, \ldots, y_n)$ let us denote by $min_x\ R(x, y_1, \ldots, y_n)$ the least x satisfying $R(x, y_1, \ldots, y_n)$ or 0 if such an x does not exist. A class K of functions is closed under the effective min-operation if together with each function $f(x, y_1, \ldots, y_n)$ satisfying the "effectivity-condition" $\bigwedge\limits_{y_1 \cdots y_n} \bigvee\limits_{x} [f(x, y_1, \ldots, y_n) = 0]$ it contains the function $min_x\ [f(x, y_1, \ldots, y_n) = 0]$.

Kleene [97] developed the theory of computable functions assuming (essentially) the following definition: a function is computable if it belongs to each class which contains the primitive recursive functions and which is closed with respect to the operations of substitution and of the effective minimum. Kleene's original definition was simpler in that he started with an incomparably smaller set of functions.

This arithmetical definition was discussed by J. Robinson [177] who showed how to simplify it still further. In particular she showed that the min-operation may be replaced by the operation of taking the inverse of a function under the assumption that it exists.

A set is computable if its characteristic function is computable. An entirely different definition was proposed not long ago by Kleene [106] in connection with his theory of functionals which will be discussed in lecture VIII; see p. 78.

3. *Canonical systems, Turing machines and algorithms.* Post [160], Turing [234], and Markov [139] proposed still other definitions of computability. A function is computable according to these definitions if it is representable in suitable auxiliary systems. These systems differ, however, from the logical systems dealt with in the definitions given in section 1 in that it is not possible to give any semantic interpretation of them. These auxiliary systems are called canonical systems, Turing machines, and algorithms. Let us describe *e.g.* the algorithms of Markov [139].

For this purpose we consider words in a given finite alphabet A, *i.e.* finite (possibly void) strings of elements of A. If g, g' are two words, then we denote by "$g \to g'$" a rule of transformation which carries a word of the form PgQ into $Pg'Q$; it is assumed that P does not contain the word g. An algorithm is determined by a finite list of such operations:

$$g_1 \to g'_1, \; g_2 \to g'_2, \ldots, \; g_k \to g'_k.$$

Some of these operations are singled out and called the "stop operations". (Markov distinguishes them by placing a dot after them.)

Let P_0 be a word; the algorithm operates in the following way: we look for the least i such that P_0 contains g_i; we represent P_0 in the form Pg_iQ where P does not contain g_i. Now we transform P_0 according to the i-th rule and obtain the word $P_1 = Pg'_iQ$; we repeat the same steps with P_1 and obtain the word P_2; *etc.* If after n steps no operation is applicable or the last operation used was a stop-operation, then P_n is the word obtained from P_0 by the algorithm. If the process never stops, then the algorithm is not applicable to P_0. We thus see that an algorithm determines a function whose domain consists of words (not necessarily of all words) and whose values are words.

Let us now assume that the alphabet contains the symbol 1, and let $\bar{n}$ be the word 11 . . . 1 (n times). A function f is called computable if there is an algorithm such that all numerals $\bar{n}$ belong to its domain and that for each n the algorithm transforms $\bar{n}$ into $\overline{f(n)}$.

As we see, this definition uses notions closely connected with the theory of computers; this connection is still closer in the case of the definition given by Turing, which we shall not reproduce here.

One of the early results of the theory of computable functions was that all the definitions which we enumerated above are equivalent to each other.

Before discussing the properties of computable functions we shall compare the various definitions. None of the definitions is strictly finitistic. In the first group of definitions we require that the representing formulae F be decidable, $i.e.$ that for every n there be a proof of either $F(\bar{n})$ or of $\neg F(\bar{n})$; in the second group of definitions we require that the min-operation be applied only to functions satisfying the condition: for every $y_1, \ldots, y_n$ there is an x such that $f(x, y_1, \ldots, y_n) = 0$; in the definition based on the notion of algorithm we require that for each integer n the word $\bar{n}$ belong to the domain of the algorithm. These non-finitistic requirements are needed to exclude the construction of the diagonal function.

In order to eliminate these infinitistic conditions it is necessary to replace computable functions by the more comprehensive class of partial computable functions which differ from the total ones in that they need not be everywhere defined. The simplest possible definition is that given in terms of an algorithm. Every algorithm determines a partial recursive function; its domain consists of integers n such that the algorithm yields a final value when applied to $\bar{n}$ and that this value is a numeral.

For the set of all partial computable functions there exists a universal partial computable function, $i.e.$ a function u with two arguments satisfying the following condition: For every partial computable function f there is an integer e such that the functions f and $\lambda x \, u(e, x)$ have the same domain and that $f(x) = u(e, x)$ for every x in the domain of f. We define $u(n, x)$ as an integer y such that the n-th algorithm eventually stops when applied to $\bar{x}$ and yields the value $\bar{y}$. The algorithms are enumerated $e.g.$ by the Gödel numbers of the defining sequences $g_i \to g'_i$.

The diagonal function $u(e, e) + 1$ is still partial computable and hence representable as $u(q, e)$. We are not led to an inconsistency because we have no right to replace e by q here: since u is only a partial function we don't know whether q is in its domain or not.

A set which is void or which is the set of values of a computable (total or partial) function is called recursively enumerable. Other, equivalent definitions of a recursively enumerable set are: the set of values of a primitive recursive function; the domain of a partial computable function; the set weakly representable in *e.g.* Peano's arithmetic. While computable functions serve to make precise the notion of decidability, recursively enumerable sets make precise another notion, *viz.* that of a set generated from given initial elements by a systematic process. For instance, formulae provable in an axiomatic theory based on a finite number of axioms are generated from the axioms by the rules of proof. The domain of a partial recursive function is recursively enumerable. The generating process is in this case the following: we write down one after the other all possible sequences of words and retain only those sequences each term of which (with the exception of the first) is obtained from the previous one by the use of the algorithm. We also reject those sequences whose last term although obtained by a non-stop operation can still be transformed by the basic operations of the algorithm and also those sequences whose first or last term is not a numeral. The required set consists of integers n such that $\bar{n}$ is the first term of one of the remaining sequences.

Post [160] formulated a method of developing the theory of recursively enumerable sets independently of the theory of computable functions. His ideas were very similar to those of Markov. Once the theory of recursively enumerable sets is developed, we can introduce the notions of computable sets and functions. This possibility is a consequence of the following theorems:

(1) The characteristic function of a set X is computable if and only if X and the complement of X are both recursively enumerable.

(2) A partial function f is computable if and only if the set of pairs $<x, f(x)>$ is recursively enumerable.

Theorem (1) can be proved as follows: Let us assume that there are two systematic processes which generate X and $-X$. By looking through the elements generated by them we must eventually come to any x given in advance. If x is generated by the first process we put $f(x) = 0$, otherwise $f(x) = 1$. Thus we have a method of calculating the value of f in a finite number of steps.

The general theory of computable functions and of recursively enumerable sets is an elegant and at the same time not very difficult mathematical theory. We shall give below the most important results. For the most part they were first established by Kleene [97].

At the beginning we have a series of elementary theorems stating the closure properties of the class of (total and partial) computable functions under such operations as substitution, recursion, inversion, *etc*. Applied to recursively enumerable sets these theorems yield the result that the class of these sets is closed under cartesian multiplication and under the operations of forming finite unions and intersections and of forming images and counter-images by means of computable functions. All these theorems are obvious if one defines computable functions by means of representability in a sufficiently strong formal system. Next few theorems deal with universal functions. As indicated above, there exists a computable partial function with two arguments which is universal for computable partial functions with one argument. It follows immediately that there exists a set-valued function F such that (a) each recursively enumerable set X is representable as $F(n)$ for a suitable n; (b) the set $\{<m, n> : m \in F(n)\}$ is recursively enumerable. In the language of algorithms this theorem says that there exists a universal algorithm U (or a universal Turing machine), *i.e.* one which is able to generate any algorithmically generable set. Thus if an algorithm A is described by the operations $g_i \to g'_i$ $(i = 1, 2, \ldots, s)$ and if it transforms a word W_0 consecutively into $W_1, W_2, \ldots, W_k$, then U acts on pairs of the form $P_j = <W_j, <<g_1, g'_1>, \ldots, <g_s, g'_s>>>$ and transforms P_j into P_{j+1} for $j = 1, 2, \ldots, k$ and finally P_k into W_k.

The existence of a universal function allows us to construct by the diagonal procedure effective examples of sets which are not recursively enumerable and also of recursively enumerable sets whose complements are not recursively enumerable. These examples serve as a starting point for a study of various decision problems. As examples of such problems we may quote the following problems:

Is there an algorithm to decide whether for any two given integers n_1, n_2 the sets $F(n_1)$ and $F(n_2)$ are identical? Is there an algorithm to decide whether two given algorithms define one and the same function?

The answer to both these questions is negative.

Computable functions (total and partial) are important for the general philosophy of mathematics not only because they allow us to express precisely the decision problem and to solve it in many special cases. Their philosophical importance is due to the fact that they can be accepted as a basis of a nominalistic mathematics. This nominalistic trend rejects such abstract notions as sets, functions, *etc.* and admits only those objects which can be named. Computable partial functions are thus evidently acceptable to the nominalists. It is another question whether it is possible to construct reasonable mathematical theories while not accepting any objects besides the computable partial functions. The negative solution of the decision problems formulated above shows that such a mathematical theory would necessarily be non-extensional, which indicates the degree of discrepancy between the nominalistic and the classical approach. These problems will be dealt with in a more detailed way in lecture XI.

There are obviously nominalistic theories of mathematics which admit more objects than just computable functions. Set-theoretically minded mathematicians of the thirties, grouped around Lusin in Moscow and around Sierpiński in Warsaw, developed the theory of Borel sets and of analytical sets which was initiated by the French semi-intuitionists of whom Borel, Baire, and Lebesgue were the best known representatives. Instead of reducing all mathematical notions to integers the semi-intuitionists started from the notion of a real number; sets of such numbers and functions defined on the set of all real numbers were not taken for granted; semi-intuitionists insisted that only nameable sets and functions are admissible. We do not have to enter into the details of what was meant by "nameable" in this context; all that we want to say here is that the theory of sets and of functions acceptable to the semi-intuitionists shows striking analogies to the theory of computable functions. The best explanation of this analogy has been given by Addison [1], [2]. We can thus see that the similarity between the philosophical programs which underlie the theory of computable functions and what is known as the descriptive theory of sets determined to a certain extent the results of these theories.

More technical applications of the theory of computable functions are furnished by various meta-mathematical theorems. We may mention *e.g.* a result of Rosser [187] who strengthened Gödel's incompleteness theorem by showing that the set of (the numbers of) undecidable arithmetical sentences is not recursively enumerable. There have also been attempts to apply the notion of a computable function to make precise the notion of a random sequence occurring in some axiomatic formulations of probability theory (Church [20]). Finally there have been several attempts to construct a computable analogue to the usual set theory and in particular to the theory of well-orderings. These attempts started with the early papers of Church [18] and of Church and Kleene [22]; the subsequent developments will be reported on in lecture XI.

To conclude our account of the early phase of computability theory let us compare once more this theory with semantics. In both these theories we define a class of abstract objects by means of linguistic concepts (we disregard for a moment the purely arithmetical definitions of computable functions). In semantics the language in question could not be purely formal but had to be interpreted. In the theory of computability the situation is different: the language need not be understood; it is sufficient to know how to manipulate its expressions. We can thus say that the theory of computability is purely syntactic. This explains the close ties between this theory and the theory of mathematical machines. The interpretation of a language is defined by means of set-theoretical concepts, which gives rise to the close relations between semantics and the set-theoretical, infinitistic philosophy of mathematics; whereas the theory of computability leans towards a more finitistic nominalistic philosophy.

Lecture V

Theorems of Herbrand and of Gentzen

Herbrand and Gentzen, who worked independently of each other along the lines of Hilbert's program, discovered important theorems which deeply influenced later research in the field of logic. We shall first deal with the work of Herbrand which was somewhat earlier than that of Gentzen. Herbrand's main results are contained in his dissertation [79]. We shall not describe all the results which it contains but shall limit ourselves to what is known as his fundamental theorem. It contains a reduction (in a certain sense) of predicate logic to propositional logic. Of course this reduction cannot be complete because the former theory is undecidable and the latter decidable.

Herband correlates with each formula F of the predicate calculus an infinite sequence of propositional formulae having the form of a disjunction:

$$H_n(F) = H_n = A_1 \vee \ldots \vee A_n;$$

these formulae are called the Herbrand disjunctions. The definition of H_n is effective, $i.e.$ H_n can be obtained from F and n by means of a fixed algorithm. The relationship between F and its Herbrand disjunctions is the following: F is provable in the predicate logic if and only if there is an n such that H_n is a theorem of the propositional calculus.

Let us give an example of how the disjunctions H_n are to be formed. Suppose that F is the formula $\bigwedge_x \bigvee_y \bigwedge_z M(x, y, z)$ where M is quantifier-free. Let φ be an arithmetical function such that $\varphi(i) > i$ and $\varphi(i) < \varphi(j)$ for all integers i, j satisfying the inequalities $1 \le i < j$; we may take as φ $e.g.$ the function $(i + 1)^2 + i$. We form the disjunction

$$(*) \qquad \bigvee_{i \le n} M(x_1, x_i, x_{\varphi(i)})$$

and replace in it every atomic formula by a propositional variable in such a way that different atomic formulae are replaced by different propositional variables. The resulting formula is the n-th Herbrand disjunction.

The formula (*) may be interpreted in the following way (*cf.* Kreisel [112]): Suppose that we are trying to build a counter-example to the formula F. We will then look for an element a and a function f correlating with each p an element $f(p)$ such that $\neg M(a, p, f(p))$ is true. Let us substitute for p arbitrary values $p_1, \ldots, p_n$; thus the conjunction

$$\bigwedge_{i \leq n} \neg M(a, p_i, f(p_i))$$

is true. The formula (*) may thus be interpreted as a statement that whatever our choice of a and of the function f will be, our attempt to build a counter-example to F will fail in the field of at most n elements.

It is very easy to show by induction on n that if (*) is provable in the propositional calculus, then F is provable in the predicate logic. We have only to note that the variable $x_{\varphi(n)}$ occurs exclusively in the last term and that we can therefore use the rule of proof

$$(1) \qquad \frac{A \vee B(x)}{A \vee \bigwedge_z B(z)}$$

and obtain the formula $\bigvee_{i \leq n-1} [M(x_1, x_i, x_{\varphi(i)}) \vee \bigwedge_z M(x_1, x_i, z)]$.
Using the rule

$$(2) \qquad \frac{A \vee B(x)}{A \vee \bigvee_y B(y)}$$

we obtain similarly $\bigvee_{i \leq n-1} M(x_1, x_i, x_{\varphi(i)}) \vee \bigvee_y \bigwedge_z M(x_1, y, z)$.
Continuing in this way and using the rule

$$(3) \qquad \frac{q \vee p \vee p}{q \vee p}$$

we obtain finally $\bigvee_y \bigwedge_z M(x_1, y, z)$, whence by the rule

$$(4) \qquad \frac{C(x_1)}{\bigwedge_x C(x)}$$

we obtain F.

It is slightly more difficult to prove, conversely, that if F is provable in the predicate logic, then there is an n such that (*) is provable in the propositional logic. The simplest way of obtaining this result is to use the completeness theorem which will be discussed in the next lecture. Herbrand himself came very close to the discovery of this theorem and probably did not make the decisive step only because he was constrained by the finitistic attitude which he had taken over from Hilbert's school. Instead of this simple and natural way of proving his theorem he used another, more difficult one. It was shown a year ago that his proof was fallacious [28]. A correct, strictly finitistic proof was given by Bernays [81].

The proof sketched above has some remarkable consequences. The only rules used in the derivation of F from (*) are (1)—(4); if (*) is provable in the propositional calculus, then it can be obtained from the axioms of the form $p \vee \neg p$ by the repeated use of the rule (3) and suitable other rules of propositional logic, *e.g.*

$$(5) \qquad \frac{p}{p \vee q}, \quad \frac{p, q}{p \wedge q}, \quad \frac{p \wedge (q \vee r)}{(p \wedge q) \vee (p \wedge r)}, \ldots$$

together with rules allowing us to change the order of formulae in disjunctions and conjunctions. In order to obtain a complete set of rules for the predicate calculus we must still add rules allowing us to bring every formula to a prenex normal form. An example of such rules is the following: If the formula $\neg \bigwedge_{x} A(x)$ is a part of another formula B, then it can be replaced throughout B by $\bigvee_{x} \neg A(x)$; and conversely.

As we see, Herbrand's theorem allows us to get rid of the classical rule of *modus ponens* altogether. Herbrand wrote: "A cause des difficultés que l'on risque de rencontrer, dans certaines démonstrations par récurrence sur les démonstrations, du fait de la règle d'implication, nous considérons ce résultat comme très important". The importance which Herbrand had in mind can be explained thus. Let us first define by induction the notion of a subformula of a given formula: For any formula A, A is a subformula of A itself; if A is a subformula of B, then it is a subformula of the formulae $B \wedge C$, $B \vee C$, $B \to C$, $\neg B$ and also of $C \wedge B$, $C \vee B$, and $C \to B$, and finally of $\bigwedge_{x} B$ and of $\bigvee_{x} B$ where x can be replaced by any variable; if $A(x)$ is a subformula of B, then so is $A(y)$ (letters x and y may again be replaced by any variables). Now Herbrand's remark amounts to the following: If F is provable, then there exists a proof of it consisting exclusively of subformulae of F. It is obvious that this result greatly simplifies the study of formal proofs. Because of the clause that $A(y)$ is a subformula of B whenever $A(x)$ is we cannot expect to obtain a solution of the decision problem, but at any case we see that we came very close to it.

Many of Herbrand's results were rediscovered and greatly improved by Gentzen [50] who devised a new logical calculus essentially equivalent to the one used by Hilbert's school but much more flexible.

Gentzen's calculus does not operate with single formulae but with sequences of the form

$$A_1 \ldots A_k \vdash B_1 \ldots B_l \quad (k \ge 0, l \ge 0)$$

where the A_i and the B_j are formulae in the usual sense. This sequence is read: At least one of the formulae $B_1, \ldots, B_l$ follows from the assumptions $A_1, \ldots, A_k$. A void string in antecedent means a true assumption and a void string in the consequent means a false conclusion. The only axioms of the Genzen calculus have the form $A \vdash A$. The rules of proof are more numerous than in the usual systems of logic; for every propositional connective we have a pair of rules allowing us to introduce this connective in the antecedent or in the consequent. For instance, the rules for the connective $\neg$ have the form

$$\frac{A_1 \ldots A_k\ X \vdash B_1 \ldots B_l}{A_1 \ldots A_k \vdash B_1 \ldots B_l\ \neg X} \qquad \frac{A_1 \ldots A_k \vdash B_1 \ldots B_l\ X}{A_1 \ldots A_k\ \neg X \vdash B_1 \ldots B_l}$$

Gentzen admitted furthermore a number of rules (called structural rules) which allow us to change the order of formulae in the antecedent and in the consequent and to avoid repetitions of formulae. A final rule called "cut" corresponds to the classical "*modus ponens*" and reads

$$\frac{A_1 \ldots A_k \vdash M\ B_1 \ldots B_l; \quad M\ C_1 \ldots C_p \vdash D_1 \ldots D_q}{A_1 \ldots A_k\ C_1 \ldots C_p \vdash B_1 \ldots B_l\ D_1 \ldots D_q}$$

Now Gentzen's main result says that this last rule is superfluous; every sequence provable by means of it is also provable without it. (A generalization of this theorem was given by Kleene [101].)

For the classical logic Gentzen's theorem yields probably nothing more than Herbrand's fundamental theorem. The flexibility of the Gentzen method is nevertheless obvious from the fact that it is applicable to many non-classical systems and especially to the intuitionistic system. Gentzen's intuitionistic calculus is not as symmetric as the classical calculus since the rule of introduction of the symbol ¬ in the antecedent must be dropped and the other rules reformulated in such a way that no sequence with more than one formula occurs as a consequence in any proof. With these limitations Gentzen's theorem on the elimination of cuts is still valid. It is the basis of various meta-mathematical results concerning the intuitionistic logic. *E.g.* it is obvious from this theorem that the intuitionistic propositional calculus is decidable. It may also be shown easily that certain formulae of the intuitionistic predicate logic are not provable intuitionistically. Proofs of this kind proceed by checking all the possible rules that could lead to the formula in question and by showing that none of them is able to yield this result. This is the case *e.g.* with the formula $\bigwedge_{x} [p \lor F(x)] \to [p \lor \bigwedge_{x} F(x)]$.

The Gentzen method is applicable to many other non-classical systems, *e.g.* to the minimal logic (*cf.* Ketonen [94]). It is also possible to apply it to systems based on certain infinitistic rules of proof. For instance, Schütte [195] has given a Gentzen style formalization of an arithmetic based on an infinitistic rule which is known as the rule ω and which allows us to obtain the general statement $\bigwedge_{x} F(x)$ from the infinite set of premisses $F(\bar{0})$, $F(\bar{1}), \ldots$. He has also used it in consistency proofs of certain arithmetics.

We shall now describe some applications of the theorems of Herbrand and of Gentzen.

The effectivity of existential statements. Let T be an axiomatic theory of the first-order based on the usual logic and on an arbitrary number of open axioms, *i.e.* of axioms in which no quantifiers occur. We assume that the primitive notions of T are relations, functions, and constants. Any meaningful combination of constants, variables and functions is called a term. Now let us assume that the formula $\bigwedge_{x} \bigvee_{y} F(x, y)$ is provable in T. Applying the Herbrand—Gentzen theorem we can show that there are a finite number of terms $t_1, \ldots, t_s$ involving only the variable x such that the disjunction $\bigvee_{i \leq s} F(x, t_i(x))$ is provable in T without using any quantifiers in the proof. We can thus say that all the existential statements provable from open axioms are effective; in other words, that if all existential assumptions in the axioms are made explicit, then all existential theorems will also be explicit. We have a corresponding, although slightly more complicated theorem for formulae with more than two quantifiers, $e.g.$ $\bigwedge\limits_{x} \bigvee\limits_{yz} \bigwedge\limits_{tz} \bigvee\limits_{uv} F(x, \ldots, v)$.

The general consistency theorem (Bernays [81]). This theorem allows us to eliminate in certain circumstances all set-theoretical notions from consistency proofs obtained by means of models. Let us assume that we are given an arithmetical model of an axiomatic system in which all the axioms of the system are true. Thus the elements of the model are integers and its relations are arithmetically defined. An axiom, $e.g.$ $\bigwedge\limits_{x} \bigvee\limits_{y} \bigwedge\limits_{z} \bigvee\limits_{t} F(x, y, z, t)$, will be called effectively true in M if there are computable functions f, g satisfying the condition $\models_M F(m, f(m), n, g(m, n))$ for all integers m, n. Now Bernays' theorem says that if all the axioms are effectively true in a model M, then so are all the consequences of these axioms. It is evident that this theorem is closely related to the previous one dealing with effectivity.

Let us consider as an example Peano's axioms for arithmetic with the schema of induction

$$\bigwedge_{y} \left\{ \bigwedge_{x} [x < y \to A(x)] \to A(y) \right\} \to \bigwedge_{x} A(x)$$

limited to formulae $A(x)$ in which no quantifiers occur. It is not difficult to prove that these axioms are effectively true in the usual arithmetical model; hence so are the theorems. Hence the formula $\bigvee\limits_{x} A(x)$ is provable if and only if there is an integer n such that $A(\bar{n})$ is provable; from this we may infer that the system in question is consistent.

Let us dicuss this result more closely. Once a model of a system is given and once the axioms are shown to be true in the model, it is trivial from the point of view of semantics to infer that the system is consistent. The point of Bernays' consistency theorem is that it does not use semantics and that it dispenses with set-theoretical constructions altogether. It is true that we used the semantic relation $\models_M F(m, f(m), n, g(m, n))$ in the formulation of Bernays' theorem. Since F is quantifier-free it is clear, however, that this relation can be defined directly without the whole elaborate semantic theory.

This elimination of set-theoretical constructions from a consistency proof is important not only from the methodological point of view. There are cases (admittedly rather rare ones) where this elimination can yield genuinely new results. A case in point is the problem whether a finitely axiomatizable fragment of Peano's arithmetic can be proved consistent within the full arithmetic. There is no hope of using the general semantic method here, for Peano's arithmetic is far too weak to allow a reconstruction of even the very limited part of semantics which is needed to prove the consistency of a finitely axiomatizable subsystem of arithmetic. (For a profound discussion of these rather intricate matters see Montague [144].) Let us also remark that the possibility of formally proving the consistency of finitely axiomatizable fragments of arithmetic within the whole of arithmetic was the basis of the work of Kreisel and Wang [117] dealing with the lengths of formal proofs.

We shall mention one more result of Gentzen which, although less general, is certainly no less famous than his theorem discussed above. This is his conception of a consistency proof of arithmetic based on transfinite induction (Gentzen [51]).

An adequate formulation of the principle of transfinite induction in its full generality is possible only in set theory. Gentzen, who was working along the lines drawn by Hilbert, used a much more restricted principle which can be expressed in purely arithmetical terms. His principle has the form

$$(*) \qquad \bigwedge_y \left\{ \bigwedge_x [x \prec y \to A(x)] \to A(y) \right\} \to \bigwedge_x A(x)$$

where A is any arithmetical formula and $\prec$ an arithmetically definable well-ordering of integers. As compared with the set-theoretical transfinite induction this principle is limited in a twofold way: First, we do not speak of sets and we use the principle only to show that all integers satisfy an arithmetical formula A. Secondly, we do not formulate the principle for any well-ordering (which would require a certain amount of set theory) but only for the very special well-orderings that can be defined arithmetically for integers.

For many formulae defining well-orderings of integers the formula (*) is provable in Peano's arithmetic; hence by Gödel's second undecidability theorem such special cases of (*) cannot yield the consistency proof. Gentzen's discovery was that there is a formula $x \prec y$ which defines a well-ordering of integers of the type $\varepsilon_0 = \omega +$

4

$\omega^\omega + \omega^{\omega^\omega} + \cdots$ and which has the property that the induction principle (*) for this well-ordering allows us to prove the consistency of arithmetic. It follows that for such a well-ordering $\prec$ the principle (*) is not provable in arithmetic.

The details of Gentzen's proof are too complicated to be given here. The general idea is that to each formal proof there is defined a transfinite number $\alpha < \varepsilon_0$ called the height of the proof; it is shown that if this proof would have as its end formula $0 \neq 0$, then so would also a proof with a lesser height. Hence the existence of a formal inconsistency would violate the induction principle.

A simpler though not essentially different proof was given by Schütte [195]. We shall return to Gentzen's theorem in lecture X on the occasion of Gödel's interpretation of intuitionistic arithmetic.

By way of conclusion, let us try to evaluate the work related to Herbrand's and Gentzen's theorems from a more general point of view. There are undoubtedly two opposing trends in the study of the foundations of mathematics: the infinitistic or set-theoretical and the finitistic or arithmetical. Herbrand's and Gentzen's original discoveries belong of course to the second of these trends but the subsequent work which has been based on these results has borrowed many ideas from the first. This influence of the set-theoretical approach is clearly visible in Bernays' consistency theorem in which semantic notions are consciously imitated in finitistic terms. We may say that Herbrand's and Gentzen's methods allow us to make finitistic certain particular cases of set-theoretical constructions. This intertwining of the two trends and the influence which they have exerted on each other will also be seen clearly in almost all subsequent lectures.

Lecture VI

The completeness problem

The completeness problem was formulated by Hilbert well before the period which interests us here and solved by Gödel in 1931. It is concerned with the relations between the syntactic and the semantic conceptions of logic. The problem can be formulated in two different ways. We can either consider an uninterpreted formal calculus, described in purely syntactic terms, and try to find a semantic interpretation for it; or we can assume as given an interpreted language and look for a formal calculus with purely syntactic rules of proof which would allow us to prove all the true sentences of the language. Both formulations lead to interesting special results. We shall deal first with the former formulation, which is the one used by Gödel.

Gödel solved the problem for the predicate calculus. It is simpler, however, to formulate it for a calculus in which there are no quantifiers. In this case a solution can be obtained in a very natural way by certain algebraic constructions; an extension of these constructions leads to a solution also in the general case.

Let us start with the very simple case in which we are given a number of axioms each of which is an equation, *e.g.* $x \cdot (y \cdot z) = (x \cdot y) \cdot z$, $x \cdot y = y \cdot x$ *etc.*; the dot denotes here a binary operation which we shall call "multiplication" in order to have a word for it. The problem is to construct a model in which these axioms are true, *i.e.* to define a set and a binary operation on the elements of the set such that all the axioms are satisfied under this interpretation. In this form the problem is very well known for algebraists, who call it the problem of constructing a free system satisfying given equations. The construction runs as follows: we consider "words" in a (finite or infinite) alphabet A, *i.e.* finite sequences of symbols correlated with the elements a of A. We call two words equivalent if one of them can be obtained from the other by transforming it according to the axioms. For instance, in case of the two axioms mentioned above and of an alphabet containing symbols a, b, the words (ab) $[(ba)b]$ and $[(aa)b](bb)$ are equivalent.

The elements of the model we are looking for are the equivalence classes of words under this relation. The operation $\times$ interpreting the multiplication is defined as $[s] \times [t] = [(s)\,(t)]$ where $[s]$ denotes the equivalence class containing s.

Let us pass to a more complicated situation where the axioms are not necessarily equations but still contain no quantifiers. The axioms are thus propositional combinations of atomic formulae $R(t_1, \ldots, t_k)$ where R_1, R_2, $\ldots$ are predicates and $t_1, \ldots, t_k$ are terms. We assume that the identity predicate occurs among the R_j's and that the appropriate axioms for identity are among the axioms of the theory. A model is now determined by a set (the universe of the model), by the interpretations of the operations and by the interpretations of the predicates. We construct it in the following way: we add the symbols of some alphabet A to the theory and consider only constant terms, *i.e.* terms which contain no variables. We can repeat our previous construction: two constant terms t_1, t_2 are called equivalent if the formula $t_1 = t_2$ is provable in the theory.

The set of all equivalence classes is taken as the universe of the model; the predicate R_j is interpreted as the relation which holds between the classes $[t_1], \ldots, [t_k]$ if and only if the formula $R_j(t_1, \ldots, t_k)$ is provable. Finally, the primitive operations on these classes are defined in the same way as in the case discussed previously.

It is not difficult to show that if the theory is complete with respect to formulae containing neither variables nor quantifiers, then all the axioms of the theory come out true under the interpretation thus obtained. This is no more true if the theory is incomplete, but it is obvious how to rearrange the proof so as to obtain a solution. After adjunction of A we extend the theory to a more comprehensive one which is complete with respect to the formulae in question, and perform our construction for this extended theory.

The extension of a theory to a complete one is a meta-logical problem which possesses a very clear algebraic content. It is closely connected with the theory of representations of Boolean algebras developed by Stone [217]. Stone's representation theorem shows that every Boolean algebra B is isomorphic with a field of sets. The main tool in his theory is the concept of a filter (or an ideal) of B, *i.e.* the concept of a subset F of B such that $x, y \in F \rightarrow x \wedge y \in F$ and $x \in F \rightarrow x \vee y \in F$. A filter which is different from B but which cannot be extended to a filter different from B is called maximal. It follows from Stone's theory that every filter different from B can be extended to a maximal filter. This theorem is in fact equivalent to his representation theorem.

Formulae of a theory can be treated as elements of a Boolean algebra if we identify mutually equivalent formulae. It turns out that the filters and maximal filters of this algebra have a very simple interpretation: a filter consists of formulae provable in an extension of a given theory (obtained by an adjunction of new axioms), and a maximal filter consists of formulae provable in a consistent complete extension of the theory. It is thus seen that the solution of the completeness problem for a theory with quantifier-free axioms follows from Stone's representation theorem for Boolean algebras.

There are several methods to extend the completeness theorem to the case of the full first-order logic. One of them uses what is known as the epsilon-theorem. This theorem shows that every consistent set S of axioms can be replaced by a consistent set of quantifier-free axioms which form a set at least as strong as S. One obtains this new system by adjoining to the given theory certain new primitive operations (called Skolem or Herbrand functions). Each model of the old system can be recovered from a model of the new system simply by dropping the interpretations of the symbols not present in the old theory. The consistency proof for the extended system is not immediately obvious, however, and it is perhaps easier to prove the completeness theorem first and derive from it the ε-theorem.

Another method which does not require any extension of the list of primitive notions of a theory was invented by Henkin [76]. It rests on a deeper analysis of the maximal filters and the relations they bear to models.

Let us consider the Boolean algebra B of sentences (*i.e.* formulae without free variables) of a first-order theory $\boldsymbol{T}$ to which we add constants denoting elements of an infinite alphabet A and the axioms stating that these constants denote different objects.

Every model whose universe I is the set of equivalence classes $[t]$ of terms (without variables) determines a maximal filter F in B. This filter consists of all sentences true in the model. It is not true, however, that every filter determines a model. For instance, if a filter contains all the sentences of the form $\neg A(t)$ and in addition the sentence $\bigvee_x A(x)$, then it is clear that it corresponds to no model. It turns out that this situation is the only one which can prevent a filter to correspond to a model. If F is a maximal filter in B with the property that

(*) for every formula A with one free variable, if the sentence $\bigvee_x A(x)$ belongs to F, then so does at least one formula of the form $A(t)$,

then there is a model (with the universe I) which corresponds to the filter. Hence the completeness problem will be solved when we show the existence of a maximal filter F with the property (*). In case of a denumerable set A several such proofs are known: Rasiowa and Sikorski [172] were the first to prove this theorem by means of topological methods; Tarski (quoted by Feferman in [33]) replaced them by purely Boolean ones, and Rieger [175] used for the same purpose the representation theory of Boolean algebras.

For a non-denumerable set A these methods are not applicable, and we must either use the methods based on the ε-theorems or a (suitably adapted) method of Henkin [76]. We may note that the first hint of a completeness theorem for a non-denumerable A was given by Tarski in an appendix to [222] (*cf.* also Malcev [134]).

A fruitful method of proving the completeness theorem was devised independently by Beth [7], Schütte [195a], [195b], and Hintikka [82]. The essence of their method (which was clearly influenced by Gentzen-type formalizations of logic) is to look systematically for a possible counter-example to a given formula F. Let us sketch this proof:

We shall call a conjunctive a finite sequence of formulae, each provided with one of the symbols $+$ and $-$, *e.g.* $\alpha = <F^+, G^-, H^-, K^+ >$. The meaning of such a conjunctive is the same as that of the formula $F \wedge (\neg G) \wedge (\neg H) \wedge K$. The void sequence Λ is also counted as a conjunctive. We shall define certain operations on conjunctives. For a given conjunctive α we first determine whether it contains a pair of formulae F^+, F^-; if this is the case we put $f(\alpha, n) = g(\alpha, n) = \Lambda$ (the void sequence). Otherwise we determine the first formula F in α (*i.e.* the one farthest to the left) which is not an atomic formula. If there is no such formula F we put $f(\alpha, n) = g(\alpha, n) = \alpha$. In the remaining cases we define $f(\alpha, n)$ and $g(\alpha, n)$ as follows:

1. $F = \neg\, F_1^{\pm}$ $f(\alpha, n) = g(\alpha, n) = <\,\ldots,\, F_1^{\mp} >$

(dots represent here formulae different from F present in α);

2. $F = (F_1 \wedge G_1)^+$ $f(\alpha, n) = g(\alpha, n) = <\,\ldots,\, F_1^+,\, G_1^+ >;$

3. $F = (F_1 \vee G_1)^-$ $f(\alpha, n) = g(\alpha, n) = <\,\ldots,\, F_1^-,\, G_1^- >;$

4. $F = (F_1 \vee G_1)^+$ $f(\alpha, n) = <\,\ldots,\, F_1^+ >,$

$ g(\alpha, n) = <\,\ldots,\, G_1^+ >;$

5. $F = (F_1 \wedge G_1)^-$ $f(\alpha, n) = <\,\ldots,\, F_1^- >,$

$ g(\alpha, n) = <\,\ldots,\, G_1^- >;$

6. $F = (\bigvee_{x} F_1(x))^+$ $f(\alpha, n) = g(\alpha, n) = <\,\ldots,\, (F_1(n))^+ >;$

7. $F = (\bigwedge_{x} F_1(x))^-$ $f(\alpha, n) = g(\alpha, n) = <\,\ldots,\, (F_1(n))^- >;$

8. $F = (\bigwedge_{x} F_1(x))^+$ $f(\alpha, n) = g(\alpha, n) =$

$= <\,\ldots,\, (F_1(0))^+,\, \ldots,\, (F_1(n))^+,\, (\bigwedge_{x} F_1(x))^+ >;$

9. $F = (\bigvee_{x} F_1(x))^-$ $f(\alpha, n) = g(\alpha, n) =$

$= <\,\ldots,\, (F_1(0))^-,\, \ldots,\, (F_1(n))^-,\, (\bigvee_{x} F_1(x))^- >.$

Now for any formula F without free variables we construct a refutation tree T of F. To this end we consider the full binary tree as drawn in diagram 4,

Diagram 4.

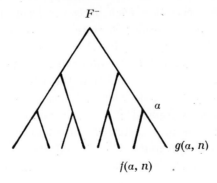

F^-

α

$g(\alpha, n)$

$f(\alpha, n)$

and place $<F^->$ in the vertex 0. We further agree that whenever a non-void conjunctive α is placed in a vertex V, then $f(\alpha, n)$ and $g(\alpha, n)$ are placed in two vertices immediately following V. The value of n (which matters only in cases $6-9$) is determined as follows: in applying rules 6 and 7 we choose as n the smallest possible integer not yet used in the tree; in the rules 8, 9, we take as n the greatest of the integers already used.

Dropping from the tree all vertices not occupied by conjunctives we obtain a refutation tree T of F. The branching points of T are all binary; hence by a well-known theorem due to König the tree is either finite or contains an infinite branch. In the former case F is provable and in the latter there is a model in which F is false. This model is defined by taking as its universe the set of all integers and interpreting a predicate, say P, as the relation R which holds between the integers $n_1, \ldots, n_k$, if and only if the formula $(P(n_1, \ldots, n_k))^+$ eventually appears in the conjunctives lying on the branch.

What is remarkable in proofs of this type is that they allow us to construct immediately a formal proof of F provided that no counter-example to it exists.

The construction sketched above differs but inessentially from the one used by Beth.

The completeness theorem found numerous applications to purely algebraic imbedding problems. It is important for such applications that the theorem be proved for a set A of arbitrarily high power. The possibility of applying the completeness theorem to such problems was first pointed out by Malcev [134] who also published the first proof of the theorem independent of the cardinality of A (Malcev's proof was not entirely correct but his mistake can easily be corrected). A typical example of the applications in question is a theorem which says that each partial ordering of a set can be extended to a complete ordering. More sophisticated applications were given by Malcev [135] and by Henkin [78].

As the most important meta-mathematical application of the completeness theorem we mention the result that an incomplete theory based on the first-order logic always has at least two non-isomorphic models. Indeed, if F is a formula which is neither provable nor refutable in a theory T, then theories T' and T'' obtained from T by adding F and $\neg F$ to its axioms are consistent and thus have models which of course are non-isomorphic. We can prove similarly that if T is an essentially incomplete theory, then it has $2^{\aleph_0}$ non-isomorphic denumerable models. In particular, Peano's arithmetic has $2^{\aleph_0}$ non-isomorphic denumerable models. The existence of such models was first proved by Skolem [209]; the proof sketched above was indicated by Gödel in a review of Skolem's paper.

The completeness theorem can also be used to establish the existence of non-isomorphic models of certain *complete* theories. Let us take as an example a consistent extension T of Peano's arithmetic. By adding Skolem functions we obtain a theory T' which is based on axioms none of which contains quantifiers. We know already that every model of T' determines a model of T. Now we add to T' a new constant a, obtaining a theory $T'(a)$. As was already pointed out above, every complete extension T^* of $T'(a)$ determines a model whose universe is the set I of all terms of $T'(a)$. The question is now how many such complete extensions T^* of $T'(a)$ there are. In order to answer this question we look at the Boolean algebra B' of all formulae of T with one free variable x. The set of formulae $F(x)$ such that $F(a)$ belongs to T^* is clearly a maximal filter in B', and every such filter determines a complete extension of $T'(a)$. Since, in the case of arithmetic, there are $2^{\aleph_0}$ maximal filters in B', we obtain $2^{\aleph_0}$ models. A model M^* corresponding to a complete extension T^* of $T'(a)$ can be isomorphic to a model M^{**} corresponding to a different complete extension T^{**} of $T'(a)$, but the number of such exceptional extensions T^{**} is at most denumerable since in the isomorphism between M^* and M^{**} the element a can be mapped only on one of denumerably many terms, and the image of a determines already the image of the whole of M^*. It follows that there are $2^{\aleph_0}$ non-isomorphic denumerable models.

We thus see that the existence of mutually non-isomorphic denumerable models of a complete theory depends not on the structure of the Boolean algebra B of sentences but on the structure of the algebra B' of formulae with free variables. The importance of this algebra was first noted by Ryll-Nardzewski [188]; we shall say more about it later when discussing the theory of models.

Several important problems arise when we consider the effectivity of the methods used in the proof of the completeness theorem. We have here really two problems: one concerning methods used to prove the existence of at most denumerable models, and the other concerning methods used to prove the existence of models of any car-

dinality. Let us start with the second problem, which clearly belongs
to the abstract set theory.

   After the discussion above it should be clear that the completeness
theorem is a consequence of the theorem known as the fundamental
theorem of Boolean filter theory, which states that every proper
filter in a Boolean algebra B can be extended to a maximal filter.
It is easy to show that this theorem is in fact equivalent to the
completeness theorem for systems of logic in which we allow an
arbitrary number of individual constants (*cf*. Łoś [125]). The fundamental theorem is known to follow from the axiom of choice; it
has also been proved that it is independent of the axioms of set
theory without the axiom of choice (*cf*. [123]). The more difficult
question whether the axiom of choice is equivalent to the fundamental
theorem has recently been answered negatively by Halpern [72].

   Let us now consider the construction of denumerable models; we
can assume that the elements of our models are integers. The natural
question to ask here is whether the models one obtains by using the
completeness theorem are always recursive or at least recursively
enumerable. To make the question more explicit let us assume that
F is a formula with (say) one binary predicate. An interpretation
of F in the set N of integers is a binary relation, *i.e.* a set R of ordered
pairs. The problem is to find out whether there is a recursively
enumerable R such that F is true in the model $<N, R>$. The answer
to this problem is negative. An example of a formula for which there
exists no recursively enumerable model is provided *e.g.* by the conjunction of all the axioms of set theory (in the formulation of Gödel
[60]). This example is due to Rabin [165].

   Kleene [104] and Hasenjaeger [75] showed that one can always
find a model in which R is defined in the form

$$m \, R \, n \equiv \bigwedge_{x} \bigvee_{y} S(m, n, x, y)$$

and in the dual form

$$m \, R \, n \equiv \bigvee_{x} \bigwedge_{y} S'(m, n, x, y)$$

with recursive S and S'. Putnam [163] obtained an even simpler form

$$m \, R \, n \equiv \bigvee_{p=0}^{q} [\bigvee_{x} S_p(m, n, x) \wedge \bigwedge_{y} \neg S'_p (m, n, y)]$$

with recursive S_p and S'_p.

Putnam's result is the best possible one for formulae without the predicate of identity; for formulae with this predicate we can impose an additional requirement on the model to the effect that the predicate of identity be interpreted as identity. The exact form of the simplest definition of a model is not known in this case.

Worth noting here are some strange features of the recursive models of certain simple axioms. For instance, Peano's arithmetic is known to possess just one (up to isomorphism, of course) recursive model; among all the $2^{\aleph_0}$ denumerable models non-isomorphic to the usual (standard) one there is not a single one which would be recursive or even recursively enumerable (*cf.* Feferman [35], Scott [196]). It is not quite clear what causes this peculiar behaviour of various axiomatic theories and what prevents some of them from admitting recursive models at all and others from admitting more than one such model.

Several attempts have been made in the literature to generalize the completeness theorem to more comprehensive systems of logic. Let us consider *e.g.* a language which differs from the usual system of logic by containing one additional quantifier (Sx) (to be read "for at most finitely many x"), additional axiom schemas

$$\bigwedge_x \neg\, F(x) \,\rightarrow\, (Sx)\ F(x);$$

$$\bigwedge_x \left\{ F(x) \equiv [(x = y_1) \vee \ldots \vee (x = y_n)] \right\} \rightarrow (Sx)\ F(x)$$

and one additional rule of proof which allows us to obtain the formula $\neg\ (Sx)\ F(x)$ from the infinite list of formulae

$$\bigvee_x F(x),\ \neg \bigvee_{y_1} \ldots \bigvee_{y_n} \bigwedge_x \left\{ F(x) \equiv [(x = y_1) \vee \ldots \vee (x = y_n)] \right\},$$

$$n = 1, 2, \ldots$$

The completeness theorem for this infinitistic logic can be obtained by the algebraic or by the topological method and also by the Beth—Hintikka—Schütte method. This was stated explicitly by Schütte [195ª]. It is significant that the methods based on the ε-theorems do not work in this case. We shall later say more about the reasons why these methods cannot be used here.

If we pass to higher logical systems the situation becomes quite different. Let us take as an example the second-order logic. As was remarked in lecture II, the syntactic structure of this logic does not decide whether it is essentially different from the first-order logic. All depends on what kinds of models of the sentences of this logic we admit. If we do not impose any limitations, the completeness theorem will continue to hold and we obtain a completeness theorem which says that a formula which is not refutable has a model in which the second-order variables are restricted to a certain subclass of the full class of subsets of the universe. This result was first obtained by Henkin [77] whose paper has essentially contributed to a better understanding of what higher-order logic really is.

However, if we admit for our second-order logic only models in which the range of the second-order variables is the full class of all the subsets of the universe, then Gödel's first undecidability theorem shows that the completeness theorem is no more true and cannot be saved unless we decide to strengthen so the axioms and rules of proof that they will no longer be effective.

These considerations lead to a different approach to the completeness problem, which is the second approach mentioned in the beginning of this lecture. We take as a starting point not the formal calculus for which an interpretation is to be found but, conversely, a language and a class of "admissible" interpretations of it. The problem is to construct a formal calculus on the formulae of this language such that precisely those formulae are provable which are true in all the admissible models. If by a calculus one means a finite set of recursive rules, then one can in some cases use results from the recursive function theory to prove that no such calculus exists.

There are many results pertaining to the problem just indicated. It is easy to show *e.g.* that for the logic with the quantifier S interpreted in the way indicated above the solution of the problem is negative: the calculus with the infinitistic rule which we discussed cannot be replaced by a calculus with a finite number of recursive rules. This is the case simply because the set of formulae which are true in all models is not recursively enumerable. We may note that this set would be recursively enumerable if the ε-theorem were true for this logic.

If we now change the interpretation of S to read: "there are at most denumerably many elements such that . . .", then the problem admits a positive solution: using results of Fuhrken [48], Vaught [239] showed not long ago that there exist recursive rules allowing one to prove exactly the formulae which are true in every model (with this interpretation of *S*). For many other special cases the problem remains open.

As another example let us consider the following problem:

We leave the language of the predicate logic unchanged but narrow down the class of admissible models. Vaught [238] has investigated the classes of formulae which are true in all recursive or recursively enumerable models and found that none of these classes can be axiomatized by recursive rules. A similar result was found earlier by Trachténbrot [233] who found that the set of formulae true in all *finite* models is not recursively enumerable although it is a complement of such a set.

The problem which we discussed in the last few paragraphs can be formulated for various non-classical logics provided we can give them an interpretation. For instance, we may take the interval [0,1] as the set of truth-values (in the case of ordinary logic there are exactly two truth-values) and interpret the propositional connectives as functions defined in this interval and taking their values from it. Quantifiers are interpreted as functions from the subsets of [0,1] to [0,1]. We can then define the basic semantical notions in the same way as in the two-valued case and ask whether the set of formulae true in every model is axiomatizable by a finite set of recursive rules. Chang [15], Scarpellini [193] and others have achieved some results in this direction; it is hard to say, however, whether investigations of many-valued logics will eventually prove to be more than a mere curiosity.

The completeness problem is an interesting example of a question which arose from philosophical investigations concerning the relations between formal calculi and semantics and which has found many purely mathematical applications in spite of its philosophical origin. One often speaks of the relevance of mathematical logic to algebra; it is chiefly the completeness theorem that allows one to connect these two disciplines in such a way that they can deeply influence one another.

Lecture VII

Further development of the recursive function theory

Full and partial computable functions are very well suited to the needs of constructively minded mathematicians. The development of the theory of these functions lead to new notions and constructions however, which do not any more conform completely to the philosophy of constructivism. Most of these new notions were introduced by Kleene. We shall here describe some of them. They are important for purely mathematical reasons but also because they allow us to study some semi-constructivistic theories.

Relative computability. This important notion due to Kleene is best explained in terms of machines. Let f be a function with one argument defined in the set of all integers and taking on integral values. We can view such a function as a device supplying us with the information that $f(0)$ is the value of f at 0, $f(1)$ at 1, and so on. Let us imagine a machine in which this infinite amount of information is stored and which performs the same steps as an ordinary machine. In the course of calculation the machine is from time to time asked to take from the memory the value of f at a point which has been calculated before. A function g calculated by such a machine is called computable with respect to f. The number of times the machine must draw on the information about the values of f depends in general on the particular argument n which appears in the input of the machine but is always finite. Thus in order to calculate g for a given value n of the argument we need only a finite number of values $f(0)$, $f(1)$, . . ., $f(z)$, where z depends on n. Instead of this sequence we can use the single integer $p_0^{f(0)+1} \ldots p_z^{f(z)+1} = \overline{f(z)}$ which synthetizes so to speak the finite sequence of the exponents (p_j denotes the j-th prime).

Kleene [98] proved that a (partial) function computable relative to f has the form

(1) $$g(n) = U \, min_z \, (R(\overline{f(z)}, n))$$

where U is a fixed primitive recursive function and R a primitive recursive relation. In order to make this result plausible we may remark that in the course of the computation of $g(n)$ the machine performs a process which can be described arithmetically by means of an integer p. We are here invoking of course the whole machinery of Gödel numbers. The process depends on the integers $f(0), \ldots, f(z)$, i.e. p is a function of $\overline{f(z)}$ and of n. This function is a partial one not only because g is not necessarily a full function but also because p is undefined if the value of z is too small; the machine cannot complete its work if a sufficient number of the values $f(j)$ is not at hand.

A more detailed analysis shows that the dependence of p on $\overline{f(z)}$ and n is given by a recursive relation, say S, whereas the value $g(n)$ is obtained from p by a recursive operation U_1. Taking all these observations together we come to the equivalence $m = g(n) \equiv \bigvee_{z, p} [S(p, \overline{f(z)}, n) \wedge (m = U_1(p))]$ from which we obtain (1) by easy formal transformations.

A similar relativisation is possible for the notion of a recursively enumerable set: a set A of integers is recursively enumerable with respect to f if A is either void or is the set of values of a function computable with respect to f.

Degrees. (Kleene and Post [109]). If g is a partial function computable with respect to f, then we say that its degree is smaller than or equal to f: $deg(g) \leq deg(f)$. The degree of f is defined as the set of all functions g satisfying both inequalities $deg(g) \leq deg(f)$ and $deg(f) \leq deg(g)$.

The degrees form a very interesting structure and much work has been devoted to them. Let us mention a few facts found in the course of this work.

Degrees form an "upper semilattice", *i.e.* for every two degrees α, β there is a smallest degree γ which satisfies $\alpha \leq \gamma$ and $\beta \leq \gamma$. It is not true, however, that for any two α, β there is the greatest degree γ which satisfies $\alpha \geq \gamma$ and $\beta \geq \gamma$ (*cf.* [109]). The first result is almost obvious but the second requires a rather ingenious proof.

One shows easily that the cardinal number of degrees is that of the continuum. Less obvious is the fact established first by Shoenfield [205] that there exists a set of mutually incomparable degrees whose cardinal number is that of the continuum.

The lowest degree $\mathbf{O}$ consists of course of computable functions. Higher degrees can be found among the arithmetically definable functions which were first introduced by Kleene [98]. A function f is arithmetically definable if there is an arithmetical formula A which defines f, *i.e.* has the property that for every n the number $f(n)$ is the only integer m such that $A(\bar{n}, \bar{m})$ is true in the standard model of arithmetic. The number of quantifiers in A serves as a measure of the complexity of the definition. Functions which can be defined by a formula with n quantifiers but not by a formula with less than n quantifiers belong to the n-th class of the arithmetical hierarchy. In order to avoid misunderstanding we remark that the atomic formulae of A have the form $y = f(x_1, \ldots, x_n)$ where f is *any* computable function.

The simplest class after $\mathbf{O}$ consists of the characteristic functions of recursively enumerable sets. From what was said in lecture IV we infer easily that there exists a "universal" recursively enumerable set K, *i.e.* a set K such that every recursively enumerable set X is representable as $\{n : f(n) \in K\}$ with a computable f. It follows that the characteristic function c_X of X has a degree less than or equal to that of the characteristic function of K. Denoting the latter degree by $\mathbf{O}'$ we obtain $deg(c_X) \leq \mathbf{O}'$. Since there are X such that c_X is not computable we obtain $\mathbf{O}' \neq \mathbf{O}$.

Most non-computable recursively enumerable sets one encounters in mathematical logic are of degree $\mathbf{O}'$. It would be more accurate to say that their characteristic functions have this degree; for simplicity's sake we shall nevertheless identify sets with their characteristic functions.

Thus *e.g.* the set of the Gödel numbers of theorems provable in any computable extension of Peano's arithmetic has the degree $\mathbf{O}'$; also the set of (the numbers of) refutable sentences has this degree. Several sets which are not recursively enumerable also have this degree, *e.g.* the set of the Gödel numbers of undecidable sentences of any such theory, and the set of the Gödel numbers of first-order formulae which are true in every finite model etc.

Sets recursively enumerable with respect to K have again a "universal" set; the degree of its characteristic function is denoted by $\mathbf{O}''$. Evidently $\mathbf{O}'' > \mathbf{O}'$. We can define similarly the degrees $\mathbf{O}'''$, $\mathbf{O}''''$ etc.

We could start not with $\mathbf{O}$ but with any degree and form the degrees α', α'', $\ldots$ In order to obtain $(deg(f))'$ we take the degree of a function which is universal for all the functions g whose degrees are $\leq deg(f)$. Evidently this construction requires a proof that such a function exists and that its degree is determined by $deg(f)$. Thus we see that the jump operation $'$ allows us to show the existence of arbitrarily high degrees. The iteration of the jump operation does not exhaust all possible degrees. There are *e.g.* degrees greater than each of the degrees $\mathbf{O}^{(n)}$, $n = 1, 2, \ldots$.

The fine structure of the set of degrees is very complicated. The most detailed account of this difficult subject is given in [190].

The computation of the degree of a given set or — in case this set (or its characteristic function) is arithmetically definable — the determination of its place in the arithmetical hierarchy presents in general a very difficult problem. We saw examples of such problems in the previous lecture where we discussed arithmetically definable models for single formulae of the predicate calculus. Several more mathematical examples can be found in [185]. An interesting example was given by Specker [213] who considered complete extensions of Peano's arithmetic. Such extensions can never be recursively enumerable but one can find them already among sets of degree $\mathbf{O}''$; Specker showed that no Boolean combination of recursively enumerable sets (of formulae) can be a consistent complete extension of arithmetic.

The set of arithmetical formulae which are true in the standard model of arithmetic has a higher degree than any $\mathbf{O}^{(n)}$; this set therefore provides us with a simple example of a set which is not arithmetically definable.

Properties of recursively enumerable sets. These sets were studied very extensively, probably because of their relevance for mathematical logic and the theory of machines. The chief contributor to the theory was Post whose paper [160] marks the beginning of a new era in this field.

1. *Post's theorem.* It was known long ago that a set which is recursively enumerable and which has a recursively enumerable complement is computable, *i.e.* has a computable characteristic function. We proved this theorem on p. 39. Generalizing this result Post showed that if a set X as well as its complement belongs to the same class of the arithmetical hierarchy, say to the n-th one, then X is recursive relative to a set belonging to a lower class of the hierarchy, *i.e.* the degree of X is $\leq \mathbf{O}^{(n-1)}$.

The theorem reminds one of a similar result on analytical sets: a set which is analytical and whose complement is analytical is a

Borel set. The analogy is imperfect, however, as we can see from the following theorem which is true for recursively enumerable sets but false for analytical sets:

2. *Theorem on non-separable sets* (Kleene [100]). There are pairs of disjoint sets X, Y which are recursively enumerable (relative to a function f) but which cannot be separated by a set computable with respect to f. In other words there is no set R computable (relative to f) such that $X \subset R$ and $Y \subset -R$.

A simple example of such a pair is the set X of (the numbers of) arithmetical formulae provable in Peano's arithmetic and the set Y of (the numbers of) arithmetical formulae which are refutable in it. Of course the essential undecidability of Peano's arithmetic is an immediate consequence of the non-separability of X and Y. Several theories much weaker than arithmetic also possess the property of non-separability, *i.e.* the property that the set of theorems and the set of their negations are non-separable.

In another example due to Trachténbrot [233] we take as X the set of (the numbers of) formulae of the predicate calculus which are false in at least one finite model and as Y the set of (the numbers of) provable formulae of this calculus.

Inseparable sets have found numerous applications. For instance, they are used in constructing first-order formulae which have no recursively enumerable models, in a proof that Peano's arithmetic has exactly one recursive model (*cf.* lecture VI), and in several other constructions.

3. *Recursively enumerable sets of special kinds.* Post asked in his paper [160] whether there exist recursively enumerable sets of different degrees. His paper contains an account of various unsuccessful attempts to solve this problem. Post stated that the set K of the degree $\mathbf{O}'$ is in a certain sense small: For every recursively enumerable set X disjoint of K it is possible to determine effectively (from the definition of X) an integer not in $X \cup K$. Post called such a set creative. All creative sets have the degree $\mathbf{O}'$, and thus are unsuitable as possible candidates for the solution of the problem. Looking for a possible example of a recursively enumerable set of a smaller degree, Post constructed "big" recursively enumerable sets. His simple sets S have the property that $-S$ does not contain any infinite recursively enumerable sets. Still bigger are the hypersimple sets H whose characteristic property is that if F_1, F_2, $\ldots$ is any recursively enumerable sequence of finite sets, then only

finitely many F_j' s have non-void intersections with $-H$. The sets constructed by Post proved to have the degree $\mathbf{O}'$ and thus did not help him to settle the problem. They were nevertheless subjected to further study partly of a purely mathematical and partly of a meta-mathematical character. Thus *e.g.* Myhill [154] showed the recursive isomorphism of any two creative sets, and Grzegorczyk [68] showed how to obtain easy proofs of Gödel's undecidability theorem by using simple or hypersimple sets. The literature on various kinds of recursively enumerable sets accumulated so rapidly between 1950 and 1960 that it is not possible to discuss it here in detail.

4. *The Friedberg—Mučnik method.* Post's problem was solved simultaneously by Friedberg [44] and Mučnik [153] in 1956, that is full 12 years after the problem was stated. Their construction is highly technical, and we find it impossible to describe it here. We shall only say that the general plan is to obtain two recursively enumerable sets $A = \bigcup_i A_i, B = \bigcup_j B_j$ where A_i and B_j are finite sets and where neither of the sets A, B is recursive in the other. The definition proceeds by stages: at even stages $s = 2i$ we take care of the set A_i and at odd stages $s = 2j + 1$ of the set B_j.

If the characteristic function c_A of A were computable relative to c_B we would have a relation

$$(2) \qquad c_A(x) = U \, (\underset{z}{min} \; \overline{T(c_B(z)}, \, x, \, e))$$

where $T(m, n, 0)$, $T(m, n, 1)$, ... is a computable enumeration of all primitive recursive binary relations. Now the choices of A_i at the stages $s = 2i$ are performed so as to obstruct relation (2) for a value e_i, where e_i ranges over all integers as i increases. Choices of the sets B_j are similar but with the roles of A and B reversed. Of course at no stage s are the sets A, B completed, and we are in fact not obstructing relation (2) but a similar relation between the characteristic functions of the approximating sets $\underset{i \leq s/2}{\bigcup} A_i, \; \underset{j \leq s/2}{\bigcup} B_j$. Thus a special care must be taken to make sure that no further choices make the relation obstructed at some stage of the approximation to reappear in the limit. The method which assures this is called the priority method.

5. *Various applications of the Friedberg—Mučnik method.* This powerful method made it possible to solve several problems concerning recursively enumerable sets and degrees as well as their relations

to meta-mathematics. We may mention as an example the result of Sacks [190] according to which every countable partially ordered set can be embedded in the semilattice of degrees. A result due to Friedberg [46] says that there exists a "maximal" recursively enumerable set M such that the complement $-M$ is infinite but cannot be divided in two infinite parts of the form $R \cap (-M)$ and $(-R) \cap (-M)$ where R is recursively enumerable, *i.e.* that no recursively enumerable set is able to divide $-M$ into two infinite parts.

An example of a meta-mathematical application is provided by a result of Shoenfield [206] who showed the existence of an axiomatic theory (based on an infinite set of axioms) which has the property that the set of the Gödel numbers of its theorems is a recursively enumerable set of any preassigned degree $\alpha < \mathbf{O}'$. For $\mathbf{O} < \alpha < \mathbf{O}'$ we obtain an example of a theory which is undecidable but such that its undecidability cannot be proved by reduction to arithmetic. As we noted above the set of the Gödel numbers of theorems provable in Peano's arithmetic have the degree $\mathbf{O}'$. Feferman [34] gave some general criteria as to when this degree is $\mathbf{O}'$ in case of an arbitrary theory.

Recursive well-orderings. We have already remarked that the theory of computable functions and its generalizations were created for the purpose of reconstructing some fragments of classical mathematics along constructivistic or nominalistic lines. We shall say more about these attempts in lecture XI. Of course the attempts to reconstruct some parts of the classical set theory in computable terms belong to this program. We include a brief discussion of computable well-orderings already here since they will be needed in the next lecture.

Let R be a primitive recursive relation whose domain and counterdomain consist of integers. If R is a well-ordering of a recursively enumerable subset of the set N of all integers, then we say that R is a recursive well-ordering.

We know that all primitive recursive relations can be arranged in a sequence $R_0, R_1, \ldots$ in such a way that the three-argument relation $R_e(x, y)$ is computable. The set of indices e such that R_e is a recursive well-ordering is denoted by O; it plays an important role in the theory of recursive well-orderings.

The ordinal types of relations R_e, e in O, form an initial segment of the Cantorian second number class. The smallest ordinal not belonging to this segment is denoted by ω_1 and called the first non-

constructive ordinal. It is a denumerable ordinal, yet there is no
primitive recursive relation of this type. It is possible to show that
there is no arithmetically definable well-ordering which would have
the type ω_1.

Recursive well-orderings are important chiefly because they allow
us to express in purely arithmetical terms definitions which usually
are expressed in set theory. We have in mind some particular cases
of what are known as the definitions by transfinite induction.

A typical definition by transfinite induction consists of three
clauses

(i) $\qquad A_0 = A,$

(ii) $\qquad A_{\xi+1} = F\,(A_\xi),$

(iii) $\qquad A_\lambda = \bigcup_{\xi<\lambda} A_\xi \qquad$ (λ is a limit number)

where A is a set and F a function whose arguments and values are
sets. This definition is expressed in set theory because we use in it
the notion of an ordinal. If we are interested only in values of A_ξ
for $\xi < \alpha < \omega_1$, however, we can eliminate ordinals in favor of
integers ordered by a recursive relation R_e with e chosen so that the
type of R_e be α. What we define is a function $A(n)$ from integers to
sets; the three clauses of the definition now become

(i′)   if n_0 is the first integer with respect to the ordering relation
R_e, then $A(n_0) = A$;

(ii′)   if n' is the immediate successor of n in the ordering R_e, then
$A(n') = F(A(n))$;

(iii′)   if n does not have an immediate predecessor in the ordering
R_e, then

$$\bigwedge_x \{ x \in A(n) \equiv \bigvee_y \,[(y \neq n) \wedge R_e(y, n) \wedge (x \in A(y))] \}.$$

(The formula in (iii′) says that $A(n)$ is the union of the sets $A(y)$
where y precedes n in the ordering R_e.)

As we see, the set-theoretical notions have disappeared from the
definition unless they are present in F.

We can also formulate an arithmetical counterpart to proofs by
transfinite induction. Corresponding to each e in O (such that the

field of R_e consists of all integers) and to each arithmetical formula G strongly representing R_e we have an arithmetical axiom

$$(*) \quad \bigwedge_m \left\{ \bigwedge_n \left[(n \neq m) \wedge G(n, m) \rightarrow A(n) \right] \rightarrow A(m) \right\} \rightarrow \bigwedge_n A(n)$$

which says that if the truth of $A(m)$ follows from the assumption that $A(n)$ is true for all n preceeding m (in the ordering R_e), then $A(n)$ is true for all n.

For certain indices e in O transfinite definitions (i′)−(iii′) are no more powerful than ordinary explicit definitions; for some e in O and some G the axiom schema (*) is also derivable from Peano's axioms for arithmetic. However, this is not true for all e in O.

The transfinite definitions here described have been used several times to obtain extensions of incomplete systems, especially of systems of arithmetic. First steps in this direction were made by Turing [235] who tried to remove the incompleteness of arithmetic by adding to it an undecidable sentence (constructed, say, by the method of Gödel) and repeating this process indefinitely by transfinite induction. A precise formulation of this construction was given recently by Feferman [37].

Another similar application of the transfinite induction to metalogical problems was made by Shoenfield [204] who investigated what is known as the effective rule ω.

The rule ω is an infinitistic arithmetical rule of proof which says that whenever all sentences $A(\bar{0})$, $A(\bar{1})$, . . ., $A(\bar{n})$, . . . are proved, then the sentence $\bigwedge_x A(x)$ can also be considered as proved. The effective rule ω (first proposed by Novikov) strengthens the assumption: instead of requiring that for every n there is a proof of $A(\bar{n})$ we assume that there is an algorithm which produces a proof of $A(\bar{n})$ whenever $\bar{n}$ is fed into it. Of course every arithmetical statement is "provable" by a finite number of applications of the rule ω. Shoenfield showed that transfinite iterations of the effective rule ω also yield a complete system of arithmetic.

Several authors have investigated the strength of the axiom (*) and its dependence on the choice of the formula G as well as on the choice of e. It turns out that there are indices e in O for which axiom (*) is quite strong and allows one to prove e.g. the consistency of arithmetic. We shall not discuss this subject but proceed rather to an extension of the arithmetical hierarchy obtained by means of transfinite induction of the kind just described.

Lecture VIII

Hierarchies and functionals

In lecture VII we discussed a hierarchy of sets of integers, known as the arithmetical hierarchy. In mathematical practice we often encounter sets which do not belong to this hierarchy, and it is therefore natural to extend it.

The hyper-arithmetical hierarchy. One obtains it by extending the arithmetical hierarchy into the constructive transfinite.

Without going into technical details we can describe the process as follows: We first fix two arithmetically definable functions π, σ such that whenever e is in O, then so are $e' = \pi(e)$ and $e_n = \sigma(e, n)$; moreover, if the order type of R_e is $\alpha + 1$, then the order type of $R_{\pi(e)}$ is α; and if the order type of R_e is a limit number λ, then the order types of $R_{\sigma(e, n)}$ form a sequence which converges to λ.

We want to define, for each e in O, a universal function F_e whose values are sets and relations which jointly form the e-th level of the hyper-arithmetical hierarchy. If the order type of R_e is 0, then we take as F_e a universal function for the family of recursively enumerable sets and relations. If the order type of R_e is $\alpha + 1$, then we take as F_e a universal function for the family of sets and relations which can be formed from sets and relations of the e'-th class (*i.e.*, from sets and relations $F_{e'}(n)$ where $n = 1, 2, \ldots$) by means of Boolean operations and quantifiers $\bigvee_x$, $\bigwedge_x$, with x ranging over integers. Finally if the order type of R_e is a limit number λ, then F_e is a universal function for the family of sets and relations of the form $\bigcup_n F_{e_n}(f(n))$, where f is a recursive function.

If X is a set (or a relation) such that there is an e in O and an integer n such that $X = F_e(n)$, then we call X a hyper-arithmetical set (or relation).

The success of this construction is due to the circumstance that the values of e' and e_n are given by computable functions π, σ of e

and n. These functions are fixed from the beginning and constantly used in the construction of the levels.

A detailed exposition of the theory based on a definition very similar to the one given above was given by Kleene [105]. It seems to me that one obtains an easier exposition if one starts from another definition based on the notion of representability (*cf.* [71]).

We consider a formal system (S) of second-order arithmetic based on Peano's axioms for integers with the axiom of induction in the form

$$\bigwedge_X \left\{ (0 \in X) \wedge \bigwedge_x [x \in X \to x + 1 \in X) \to \bigwedge_x (x \in X) \right\}$$

and on the following set-theoretical axioms:

$$\bigwedge_x [x \in X \equiv x \in Y] \to (X = Y) \qquad \text{(extensionality)},$$

$$\bigvee_X \bigwedge_x (x \in X \equiv A(x)] \qquad \text{(comprehension)}.$$

In the axiom of comprehension $A(x)$ stands for an arbitrary formula which may or may not involve set variables but does not involve X.

In addition to the usual rules of proof we admit into (S) the (strong) rule ω (*cf.* lecture VII). We define hyper-arithmetical sets (relations) as the ones which are strongly representable in (S).

A related definition was also proposed by Kreisel [114]; he used certain model-theoretic notions, however, instead of the quasi-syntactical notion of representability in (S).

Our definition reveals the source of the close analogy between hyper-arithmetical and computable sets (relations). Indeed, both these classes are defined as consisting of sets (relations) strongly representable in a formal system; the only difference is that in order to obtain computable sets we take as this system the usual second-order arithmetic whereas the hyper-arithmetical sets are obtained if we adjoin to the second-order arithmetic an additional infinitistic rule of inference.

Of course we can introduce (total) hyper-arithmetical functions exactly in the same way as computable functions.

Several definitions used in the theory of computable sets and functions can now be repeated in the hyper-arithmetical case. We can relativize the notion of a hyper-arithmetical function by introducing sets (relations, functions) hyper-arithmetical with respect to a given set (relation, function) X. To obtain this notion we add to the symbols of (S) a new symbol $\varXi$ denoting a set and axioms $\bar{n} \in \varXi$ for those integers n which belong to X as well as axioms $\neg (\bar{n} \in \varXi)$ for those integers n which do not belong to X. Sets (relations, functions) which are strongly representable in the resulting system (S_X) are called hyper-arithmetical relative to X.

Once we have the relative notion we can define degrees, called here hyper-degrees. The hyper-degree of a set (relation, function) X is the class of sets (relations, functions) Y which are hyper-arithmetical with respect to X and have the property that X is hyper-arithmetical with respect to them.

The notion which corresponds to that of a recursively enumerable set is of course the notion of a set weakly representable in (S_X). One can show that these sets coincide with sets definable in the form $\{n : \bigwedge\limits_{X} R^X(n)\}$ where $R^X(n)$ is a relation arithmetical with respect to X. Another form in which these sets can always be represented is $\{n : \bigwedge\limits_{X} \bigvee\limits_{x} T\, (\overline{c_X(x)}, n)\}$ where c_X is the characteristic function of X, T is a recursive relation, and $\overline{f(x)}$ is equal to $\prod\limits_{i \leq x} p_i^{f(i)+1}$. Sets definable in this form are called $\varPi_1^1$-sets. An example is furnished by the set O of integers which enumerate all primitive recursive well-orderings of recursively enumerable subsets of N. The set O is universal for the family $\varPi_1^1$ exactly as the set K defined in the previous lecture was universal for the family of recursively enumerable sets: Every $\varPi_1^1$-set is representable as $\{n : f(n) \in O\}$ where f is a primitive recursive function. Thus O has the largest hyper-degree among $\varPi_1^1$-sets; we shall say that the hyper-degree of O has been obtained from the hyper-degree of hyper-arithmetical sets by the operation of hyperjump.

The analogue of Post's problem which was so difficult for degrees turns out very easy for hyper-degrees. Spector [215ᵃ] has shown that there are no hyper-degrees strictly lower than the hyper-degree of O but not hyper-arithmetical. He also proved that there are continuum many incomparable hyper-degrees. His methods are based on measure theory and category theory.

The analogue of Post's theorem is valid for $\varPi_1^1$-sets: A $\varPi_1^1$-set whose complement is also a $\varPi_1^1$-set is hyper-arithmetical. The separation theorem holds for complements of $\varPi_1^1$-sets: If A and B are disjoint and both are complements of $\varPi_1^1$-sets, then they can be separated by means of a hyper-arithmetical set. Students of set theory cannot fail to note that all these results are but for notational variation identical with classical results in what is known as the theory of analytic sets. This theory was initiated by Suslin and developed further by Lusin and Sierpiński. It deals with sets of real numbers or more generally with subsets of certain spaces and in particular with sets definable in the form $\bigvee_X \bigwedge_n T\,(\overline{c_X(n)},\,a)$ where T is a closed set and X ranges over sets of integers. We see thus a close analogy between these theories: computable relations correspond to closed subsets of the space, Π_1^1-sets to analytic complements, and hyper-arithmetical sets to Borel subsets of the space.

As an example of a result obtained by pursuing these analogies let us note the following development of a Π_1^1-set into "constituents":

For every Π_1^1-set $P = \{n : \bigwedge_X \bigvee_n T\,(\overline{c_X(x)},\,n)\}$ there exists a primitive recursive relation C such that

$$ n \in P \equiv \bigvee_{e \in o} C(e,\,n). $$

This development is an analogue of a theorem of Lusin—Sierpiński according to which an analytic complement is representable as a union of Borel sets.

The analogies between the descriptive set-theory and the hyper-arithmetical hierarchy were formulated satisfactorily for the first time by Addison [2].

The analytic hierarchy. A further extension of the hyper-arithmetical hierarchy is the analytic hierarchy of Kleene [105]. We obtain it by dividing sets into classes according to their definitions just as in the case of the arithmetical hierarchy; however, this time we allow formulae containing not only the quantifiers $\bigwedge_x$, $\bigvee_y$ whose range consists of integers but also quantifiers $\bigwedge_X$, $\bigvee_Y$ whose range consists of sets of integers. Thus an analytic class consists of sets defined by a formula in which alternating set-quantifiers $\bigwedge_X$ or $\bigvee_X$ are followed by a formula with no set-quantifiers. *E.g.* the fourth analytic class consists of sets

$$ (i) \qquad \{k : \bigvee_X \bigwedge_Y \bigvee_Z \bigwedge_T \bigvee_p M\,(\overline{c_X(p)},\,\overline{c_Y(p)},\,\overline{c_Z(p)},\,\overline{c_T(p)},\,k)\} $$

and of sets

(ii) $\left\{ k : \bigwedge_X \bigvee_Y \bigwedge_Z \bigvee_T \bigwedge_p M\left(\overline{c_X(p)},\ \overline{c_Y(p)},\ \overline{c_Z(p)},\ \overline{c_T(p)},\ k\right) \right\}$

where M is a primitive recursive relation.

Sets of the form (i) we count to the class Σ^1_4 and those of the form (ii) to the class Π^1_4.

In the same way as in the arithmetical hierarchy the classes Π^1_{s+1} and Σ^1_{s+1} contain sets of a hyper-degree higher than those of all the sets in Π^1_s and Σ^1_s. Certain questions which were easily disposed of in case of the arithmetical hierarchy are very difficult in the analytic case, however. It is not known, for instance, whether the separation theorems hold for Π^1_s-sets when $s > 2$. It seems probable that this question cannot be answered at all on the basis of the usual axioms of set theory (cf. Addison [2]).

We have restricted our account to sets whose elements are integers. In case of analytic hierarchy it is perhaps more natural to consider sets whose elements are subsets of N since such sets are admitted anyhow as values of bound variables. The theory thus generalized is for all practical purposes identical with the theory of projective sets developed in the twenties by Lusin and his school. It is known that this theory abounds in very difficult problems which cannot probably be solved on the basis of the existing set-theoretical axioms. An excellent account of interrelations between the theory of hierarchies and the descriptive theory of sets is contained in Addison's paper [2].

Meta-mathematical applications of higher analytical sets are rather scarce; Scott (unpublished) found some applications showing that sets representable in languages with infinitely long formulae are analytic.

Primitive recursive functionals. The notions of primitive recursiveness and of computability have been extended to objects of higher types; the first step in this direction was taken by Gödel in 1958 [62]. We can look at his idea as a departure from strictly finitistic conceptions (which proved to be too weak to serve as a basis for Hilbert's program) but in quite a different direction from the one which leads to the various hierarchies which we discussed above. Gödel's idea whose germ can be found in writings of Hilbert is to define the notion of computability not only for sets of integers and for functions from integers to integers but also for objects of higher logical types. These objects are called functionals.

Let us explain what functionals are. To this end we first define by induction certain type-symbols: * is a type symbol; whenever $\tau_1, \ldots, \tau_k, \tau_0$ are type-symbols, then so is $(\tau_1, \ldots, \tau_k : \tau_0)$; no other symbols are type-symbols.

Functionals of type * are integers; if $\tau = (\tau_1, \ldots, \tau_k : \tau_0)$ is a type-symbol, then functionals of type τ are functions with k arguments ranging over functionals of type $\tau_1, \ldots, \tau_k$ respectively and whose values are functionals of type τ_0. Thus *e.g.* functionals of type (* : *) are numerical functions, *i.e.* functions from integers to integers, functionals of type ((* : *) : (* : *)) are functions whose arguments and values are numerical functions *etc.*

Arbitrary functionals are of course highly infinitistic entities accessible only to set-theorists. Gödel considered a very narrow class of functionals called primitive recursive functionals which — as he showed — are very useful in meta-mathematical investigations. The definition of primitive recursive functionals is as follows (for later use we correlate with each functional f an index $Ind(f)$ which we give in parentheses):

1. A functional of type $(\tau_1, \ldots, \tau_k : *)$ with a constant value 0 is primitive recursive. (Index : $< 1, (\tau_1, \ldots, \tau_k : *) >$.

2. A functional S of type (* : *) defined by $S(x) = x + 1$ is primitive recursive. (Index : 2.)

3. If f has the type $\tau = (\tau_1, \ldots, \tau_k : \tau_0)$ and is primitive recursive, then the functional obtained from f by interchanging the p-th and the q-th argument and the functional obtained from f by an identification of the p-th and the q-th argument are primitive recursive. (Indices $< 3, p, q, Ind(f) >$ and $< 4, p, q, Ind(f) >$.)

4. If f has the type $\tau = (\tau_1, \ldots, \tau_k : \tau_0)$ and is primitive recursive then the functional g of type $(\tau_1, \ldots, \tau_k, \sigma_1, \ldots, \sigma_p : \tau_0)$ defined by the equation

$$g(v_1, \ldots, v_k, w_1, \ldots, w_p) = f(v_1, \ldots, v_k)$$

is primitive recursive. (Index : $< 5, \sigma_1, \ldots, \sigma_p, Ind(f) >$.)

The operation 4 allows us to add inessential variables to a functional.

5. If f has the type $\tau = (\tau_1, \ldots, \tau_k : \tau_0)$ and g the type $(\sigma_1, \ldots, \sigma_r : \tau_1)$ and both are primitive recursive then the functional h of type $(\sigma_1, \ldots, \sigma_r, \tau_2, \ldots, \tau_k : \tau_0)$ defined by the equation

$h(v_1, \ldots, v_r, w_2, \ldots, w_k) = f(g(v_1, \ldots, v_r), w_2, \ldots, w_k)$ is primitive recursive. (Index : $< 6, Ind(f), Ind(g) >$.)

6. If f is a primitive recursive functional of type $(\tau_{i+1}, \ldots, \tau_k : (\tau_1, \ldots, \tau_i : \tau_0))$ then the functional h of type $(\tau_1, \ldots, \tau_k : \tau_0)$ defined by the equation $h\,(a_1, \ldots, a_k) = [f\,(a_{i+1}, \ldots, a_k)]\,(a_1, \ldots, a_i)$ is primitive recursive. (Index : $<7,\ Ind(f)>$.)

7. If f has the type $(\tau_1, \ldots, \tau_k : \tau_0)$, $i \leq k$, and $g_1, \ldots, g_i$ are functionals of types $\tau_1, \ldots, \tau_i$, and $f, g_1, \ldots, g_i$ are primitive recursive then the functional h of type $(\tau_{i+1}, \ldots, \tau_k : \tau_0)$ defined by the equation

$$h\,(v_{i+1}, \ldots, v_k) = f\,(g_1, \ldots, g_i, v_{i+1}, \ldots, v_k)$$

is primitive recursive. (Index: $<8,\ i,\ Ind(f),\ Ind(g_1), \ldots, Ind(g_i)>$.)

8. The functional f of type $((\tau_1, \ldots, \tau_k : \tau_0), \tau_1, \ldots, \tau_k : \tau_0)$ defined by the equation

$$f\,(v, v_1, \ldots, v_k) = v\,(v_1, \ldots, v_k)$$

is primitive recursive. (Index: $<9,\ (\tau_1, \ldots, \tau_k : \tau_0)>$.)

9. If f and g are primitive recursive functionals of types $(\tau_1, \ldots, \tau_k : \tau_0)$ and $(\tau_0\ ^*, \tau_1, \ldots, \tau_k : \tau_0)$, then the functional h defined by recursion
$$h\,(0, v_1, \ldots, v_k) = f\,(v_1, \ldots, v_k),$$
$$h\,(x+1, v_1, \ldots, v_k) = g\,(h\,(x, v_1, \ldots, v_k), x, v_1, \ldots, v_k)$$
is primitive recursive. (Index: $<10,\ Ind(f),\ Ind(g)>$.)

Gödel gave in [62] an axiom system whose smallest model consists of primitive recursive functionals and stated that this system has the same strength as Peano's arithmetic with a strong schema of induction

$$\bigwedge_y \left\{ \bigwedge_x [x \prec y \to A(x)] \to A(y) \right\} \to \bigwedge_x A(x),$$

where $x \prec y$ is a formula which defines a well-ordering of integers into the type ε_0. No proof of this assertion has been hitherto published. It is obvious from his remark, however, that the theory of primitive recursive functionals while stronger than the ordinary Peano arithmetic is nevertheless still an intuitively clear theory which can serve as a basis for meta-mathematical investigations in the sense of Hilbert. Gödel himself showed such applications; we shall say a few words about them in lecture X.

A very elegant definition of primitive recursive functionals has been given by Grzegorczyk [69].

Computable functionals. Kleene [106] formulated a problem of extending to functionals the notion of computable partial functions.

The definition which he proposed used the machinery of indices which we introduced together with schemata defining the primitive recursive functionals. These indices represent a code in which the process of calculation of primitive recursive functionals is noted. We consider now a new schema: Let $\tau = (\tau_1, \ldots, \tau_k : \tau_0)$ be a type symbol. F_τ is a functional of type $(*, \tau_1, \ldots, \tau_k : \tau_0)$ such that if z is the index of a functional f of type τ and $a_1, \ldots, a_k$ are functionals of types $\tau_1, \ldots, \tau_k$, then $F_\tau(z, a_1, \ldots, a_k) = f(a_1, \ldots, a_k)$. We give to F_τ the index $< 11, \tau >$.

The class of functionals to which an index can be correlated according to these definitions is just the class of (partial) computable functionals in the sense of Kleene.

Kleene gave several definitions equivalent to his original one (*cf. e.g.* [107]). The whole theory is still in its first stages and it is not immediately obvious whether it will find applications to logic.

The actual computation of a Kleene's functional takes on the form of a tree. If we want to compute the value of a functional with the index z for the arguments $a_1, \ldots, a_k$ (of the appriopriate types) we investigate the form of z and reduce the computation to the computation of certain other computable functionals. *E.g.*, if $z = < 11, \tau >$ and $a_1 = q$, then we reduce the problem to finding the value of $f(a_2, \ldots, a_k)$ where f is the functional with the index q. In more complicated situation we may reduce the problem to that of finding, say, $f(a_2, \ldots, a_k)$ where f is a functional with the index $a_1(h(a_2))$ where again h is a functional with a given index r. We have then to compute first $h(a_2)$ (which need not be a number but a function or even a functional), then find the value of $a_1(h(a_2))$ which we consider as given once the functional a_1 is given and then proceed to evaluate $f(a_2, \ldots, a_n)$.

Thus we see that the computation tree of $f(a_1, \ldots, a_k)$ is in general infinite and its cardinality is very big. Though there are only denumerably many computable functionals, their class can be considered only by means of a very strong set theory.

Computable functionals of type $(* : *)$ are just the computable functions which we discussed in lecture IV. Thus Kleene's general definition of computable functionals gives us still another definition of computable functions. One can find in Kleene's [106] a detailed proof that his new definition is equivalent to the usual one.

Bar-recursive functionals. Spector [216] defined a less infinitistic extension of primitive recursive functionals. The new principle he used to define his functionals was called by him the "bar-recursion". Its simplest example can be described as follows: Let s range over finite sequences of integers: $s = <s_0, \ldots, s_{k-1}>$; we call k the length of s and denote it by $lh(s)$. We can identify s with the integer $\Pi_{i<k} p_i^{s_i+1}$. Let Y, G, and H be functionals with types $((* : *) : *)$, $(* : *)$ and $((* : *), * : *)$. We assume that $Y(f)$ depends only on a finite number of terms of f, i.e. that there is a p such that $Y(f_1) = Y(f_2)$ whenever f_1 and f_2 coincide in their first p terms. We now define the functional F of type $(* : *)$ by the following rule in which s' denotes the infinite sequence $<s_0, \ldots, s_{k-1}, 0, 0, 0, \ldots>$ and $s^\frown a$ the sequence $<s_0, \ldots, s_{k-1}, a>$:

$$F(s) = G(s) \qquad\qquad \text{if } Y(s') < lh(s),$$

$$F(s) = H(\lambda a\, F(s^\frown a), s) \qquad \text{if } Y(s') \geq lh(s).$$

The computation of F can be described thus: if $Y(s') < lh(s)$ the value of $F(s)$ is explicitly given. Otherwise we reduce our problem to that of finding the function $\varphi(a) = F(s^\frown a)$. If $Y((s^\frown a)') < lh(s^\frown a) = lh(s) + 1$, then $\varphi(a) = G(s^\frown a)$ and our computation is accomplished. Otherwise we look for the function $\psi(a, b) = F(s^\frown a^\frown b)$ etc. Because of the assumption which we made the value of Y eventually ceases to increase as we take larger and larger extensions of s. Hence after finite numbers of steps we find the functions $\varphi(a)$, $\psi(a, b), \ldots$ and hence the value of $F(s)$.

Spector generalized this idea to arbitrary types and showed that his bar-recursive functionals can be used to obtain consistency proofs for second-order arithmetic.

Let us finish this review of the various notions of computability by taking a look on the tendency which is apparent in the historical development of the subject.

We started with certain very simple notions, close to the intuitive idea of computability. The class of objects thus obtained proved to be too narrow, however. The need of having a round off theory and of finding objects which would help us to fulfil Hilbert's program forced the logicians to depart more and more from the ideal simplicity of computable functions and to introduce more and more infinitistic objects. The tools thus created have an intrinsic value and formal applications (e.g. to proofs of consistency). Whether they fit to a philosophical program of finitism or intuitionism is rather dubious.

It looks as if extreme finitism were too barren to allow really fruitful applications; we obtain however important results when we try to approach it. We shall see in the next lecture how a seemingly very modest limitation imposed on the unrestricted set-theoretical notions has led Gödel to solve important consistency questions in set theory. It seems therefore that it is better not to adhere unrestrictedly to the philosophical program of finitism which did not produce all too important results; on the other hand some limitations going into the direction shown by finitists brings extremely interesting and valuable results.

Lecture IX

Consistency of the axiom of choice and of the continuum hypothesis

In 1940 Gödel published a monograph [60] devoted to the problem of consistency of the basic set-theoretical hypotheses. His main proof was widely commented on, and it has exerted a profound influence on the meta-mathematical and philosophical work of the last two decades. In view of the importance of the topics dealt with by Gödel we shall discuss them at some length.

The consistency proof devised by Gödel is closely related to the subject developed in last two lectures. Gödel constructs a model in which the axiom of choice and the continuum hypothesis are valid by extending the arithmetical hierarchy into the transfinite. We saw in the preceding lecture that the extension of the arithmetical hierarchy into the *constructive* transfinite leads to the hyper-arithmetical sets. If we drop the assumption that the transfinite levels are to correspond to recursive well-orderings and allow arbitrary ordinals as labels of the successive levels, we obtain an incomparably larger family of sets. These sets were called by Gödel constructible sets; they form a model for all set-theoretical axioms together with the axiom of choice and the continuum hypothesis.

A constructively minded mathematician cannot understand Gödel's proof, if he is sincere, for he does not accept the notion of an arbitrary ordinal. He can only interpret this proof in a purely formal way; ordinals will then be certain objects described in the axioms of set theory. We shall not take this stand, however, but rather assume that the general notion of an ordinal is intuitively clear to us.

The family of sets defined by Gödel represents a realization of what is known as the predicative foundation of mathematics. The notion of predicativity was introduced by Poincaré at the beginning of this century. It seemed to him that we shall be able to eliminate

6

set-theoretical antinomies by considering only such sets (functions, relations) as can be defined without referring in the *definiens* to any totality involving the object which we want to define. Such definitions are called predicative.

Gödel made these intuitions precise in the following way. Let $A, B, \ldots$ be set-theoretical formulae with at least one free variable x (by a set-theoretical formula we mean a first-order formula built from the atomic formulae $x = y$ and $x \in y$). A model for a formula of this kind is furnished by an arbitrary family K of sets; in such a model the symbol $\in$ is interpreted as the relation "being an element of". Every formula A with exactly one free variable determines a subset of K consisting of those elements X in K which satisfy the condition $\models_K A[X]$. In case A has $k + 1$ free variables we can say that every choice of values $Y_1, \ldots, Y_k$ in K for any k of these variables determines together with A a subset of K:

$$\{X \in K : \models_K A [X, Y_1, \ldots, Y_k]\}.$$

The family of all sets thus obtained is denoted by $D(K)$ and called the family of set-theoretically definable subsets of K.

Gödel takes now as K_0 the void family and defines a transfinite sequence of sets by induction as follows:

$$K_{\xi+1} = D(K_\xi),$$

$$K_\lambda = \bigcup_{\xi < \lambda} K_\xi$$

(In the second formula λ is a limit number.) Every set in $K_{\xi+1} - K_\xi$ is defined without reference to the totality $K_{\xi+1}$ to which it belongs and only with reference to a smaller totality. In this sense we can say that sets which belong to any K_ξ are admissible from the predicative point of view.

The infinitistic element in this definition lies in the use of arbitrary ordinals.

Sets which belong to $K_{\xi+1} - K_\xi$ are called constructible at level $\xi + 1$. Sets constructible at any level are called constructible.

Constructible sets form again a hierarchy. Unlike the hierarchies discussed in the previous lectures this hierarchy extends into the Cantorian transfinite; we refrain on purpose from imposing any limitation on the ordinals ξ used for labelling the levels.

The following hypothesis has been called by Gödel the axiom of constructibility: Every set is constructible. One could object that this axiom is evidently false since *e.g.* the set $\{a, b\}$ consisting of two objects a, b which are not sets is certainly not an element of K_ξ for any ξ. For Gödel the word "set" has a special meaning, however: A set is a collection a_0 of objects whose members are again sets and which has the property that there are no infinite decreasing sequences ... $a_n \in a_{n-1} \in \ldots \in a_1 \in a_0$. The word "set" in the axiom of constructibility has this narrow technical sense.

Even with this limitation the axiom of constructibility is a highly dubious statement. An intuitionist would reject it outright not only because it contains various infinitistic terms but also because it states the existence of a law defining an arbitrary set while it seems more probable that there exist sets which cannot be defined by any law. Take *e.g.* a sequence of sets

$$0, \{0\}, \{0, \{0\}\}, \ldots$$

which we shall denote for short by $\bar{n}_0, \bar{n}_1, \bar{n}_2, \ldots$. An intuitionist would say that we can form a set Z by casting dice and including $\bar{n}_p$ to Z if and only if in the p-th cast we obtained an even number. Such a set Z is certainly non-constructible.

In spite of these doubts it must be admitted that the notion of an arbitrary subset of a given infinite set is not sharply defined and that different interpretations of this notion seem to exist which are all compatible with our common intuition. The axiom of constructibility represents a very definite limitation of this notion; thus various problems whose solution seems hopeless for the unlimited notion of a set can very well become solvable if we accept the new axiom.

It is one of the most difficult tasks for a mathematician to decide whether he has to accept or to reject a new axiom. If sets were real objects existing in the world in the same sense as physical bodies we could leave the decision to experiments of some kind. Since nothing supports this Platonistic assumption, we are left without any criterion of truth if we do not consider as such the formal criteria of consistency and our very unclear "mathematical intuition".

At present we must resign ourselves to the possibility that there exist two equally acceptable set theories: one which accepts the axiom of constructibility and another which rejects it. However unpleasant this situation may be for those (rare) mathematicians who maintain that mathematics discovers truth, we must say that we see no way of deciding which of these two set theories is superior to the other.

Independently of what our attitude to these philosophical questions may be, we can state various formal consequences and properties of the axiom of constructibility.

The most important result is that the axiom is consistent relative to the other axioms of set theory. Gödel proved this theorem by showing that the axiom of constructibility is true in the domain of constructible sets (which can be defined in the usual set theory), and that all set-theoretical axioms are true in this domain. The first fact is proved by an analysis of the notion of constructibility; we have to show that the definition of constructibility is not affected by a relativization of the fundamental notions of set theory to the class of constructible sets. The second fact is proved by showing that there are arbitrarily great ordinals ξ such that all set-theoretical axioms are true in K_ξ. Thus the axioms are not able to distinguish between the whole universe and certain sufficiently big sets. This is in effect a well-known principle of set theory known as the reflection principle.

It is almost obvious that the axiom of constructibility implies the well-ordering theorem. The set K_0 is obviously well-ordered, and the well-ordering of any K_ξ extends in a natural way to a well-ordering of $K_{\xi+1}$. Thus every K_ξ can be well-ordered and hence — by the axiom of constructibility — every set whatsoever can be well-ordered.

Much less obvious is the fact that the axiom of constructibility implies the generalized continuum hypothesis. In order to show *e.g.* that there are only $\aleph_1$ subsets of the continuum Gödel shows that every constructible set X of integers is constructible already at a denumerable level ξ. He thus obtains an enumeration of constructible sets of integers by means of denumerable ordinals, which is precisely the content of the continuum hypothesis.

The famous contraction lemma of Gödel which he used to prove this fact is in effect a form of the Skolem—Löwenheim theorem. According to this theorem there is a denumerable family of sets containing X and forming a model for set theory (with the axiom of constructibility). This family is then "contracted" in order to obtain a transitive family, *i.e.* a family whose all elements are among its subset. The way in which this contraction is executed is best seen on an example: If the given family is $\{A, \{A, \{A\}\}, \{A\}\}$, then the contraction yields $\{0, \{0, \{0\}\}, \{0\}\}$. The minimal element A of the given family is contracted to 0 (which is the absolutely minimal element), and other elements $\{A\}$, $\{A, \{A\}\}$ are accordingly contracted to $\{0\}$ and $\{0, \{0\}\}$.

The general principle is that if m_1, m_2, ... are contracted to m_1', m_2', ..., then the set $\{m_1, m_2, \ldots\}$ is contracted to $\{m_1', m_2', \ldots\}$.

The resulting denumerable transitive family is isomorphic with the given one and is therefore a model for the set-theoretical axioms including the axiom of constructibility. This implies (as we shall see) that this family is one of the sets K_ξ with a denumerable ξ. Since X is not affected by contraction we obtain $X \in K_\xi$.

In order to show that the sets K_ξ are the only possible transitive families A which are models for the set-theoretical axioms including the axiom of constructibility we analyze the axioms and look at the statements concerning A which express the fact that the axioms are true in A. It turns out that most set-theoretical properties do not change their content when relativized to A. If $e.g.$ P and Q are elements of A which satisfy in A the property "P is a subset of Q", then P is a subset of Q. The definitions of ordinals and of the classes K_ξ have the same property of "absoluteness". Hence if the axiom of constructibility $\bigwedge_x \bigvee_\xi (x \in K_\xi)$ is true in A, then for every x in A there is a ξ in A such that $K_\xi \in A$ and $x \in K_\xi$. It follows easily that A is the union of all the sets K_ξ which it contains, whence the theorem easily follows.

The exact proof of Gödel's theorem requires thus a meticulous discussion of the question as to which definitions are absolute. After this very tiresome discussion the proof goes through rather smoothly.

The existence of a definable well-ordering and the realization of the generalized continuum hypothesis are two properties of constructible sets which cannot be established for arbitrary sets. Another such property was found by Scott [198]. He showed that there is no set X in which there exists a constructible denumerably additive non-trivial two-valued measure which is 0 on finite subsets of X. It is still an open and apparently very difficult question whether one can assume without inconsistency that there is a set on which such a non-constructible measure exists.

The axiom of constructibility was used by Gödel already in 1939 to solve several outstanding questions in the theory of projective

sets. Meanwhile similar questions arose in the theory of analytic
hierarchies, and their solutions have been derived from the axiom
of constructibility. Gödel did not publish his results which he
merely announced in [59]; full proofs have been published by
Novikov [157] and Addison [3].

The basis of these applications is the following result: If the axiom
of constructibility is true, then there exists a definable well-ordering
of all the sets of integers. This well-ordering can be found already
in the second analytic class, i.e. it can be defined by either of the
two formulae

$$\bigvee_{Z} \bigwedge_{T} \bigvee_{n} R\,(X,\,Y,\,\overline{c_Z(n)},\,\overline{c_T(n)}),$$

(*)

$$\bigwedge_{Z} \bigvee_{T} \bigwedge_{n} S\,(X,\,Y,\,\overline{c_Z(n)},\,\overline{c_T(n)})$$

with recursive functionals R, S.

It is easy to prove that no simpler definition of a well-ordering of
sets of integers is possible.

The construction of these formulae is not difficult. We saw that
every constructible set of integer is an element of K_Ω and that there
exists a well-ordering of K_Ω. The elements of K_Ω are denumerable
and their elements as well as the elements of their elements etc. are
denumerable and it is possible to map constructible sets of integers
in a one-one way into the elements of K_Ω. The well-ordering of K_Ω
goes then over into a well-ordering of the constructible sets of integers. Analyzing the definition of this relation we find that it can
be reduced to either of the two forms (*) while the axiom of constructibility implies that we obtain in this way a well-ordering of
all the sets of integers.

We can say, in short, that the existence of a definable well-ordering
has been proved by expressing the theory of the set K_Ω in the language of the second-order arithmetic. This arithmetization is presented in an especially clear way in [3].

The existence of a definable well-ordering allows us to solve many
problems concerning the analytic hierarchy. Addison [2] has discussed
the problem of separability for the analytic hierarchy and found
that any two disjoint sets which belong to the n-th class Π_n^1 of the
analytic hierarchy $(n > 1)$ are separable by means of sets which
belong to the n-th class together with their complements. For sets
whose definitions begin with an existential quantifier the theorem is

false. The situation is thus exactly the reverse to what we find in the first analytic class.

Several other mathematical applications have been discovered by Kuratowski [118]. Machover [133] used the axiom of constructibility in discussing an extension of the notion of computability to the theory of functions of ordinal variables. His computable functions were defined by an infinite system of equations. In order to repeat the diagonal construction he had to construct a computable correspondence between ordinals and systems of equations. The existence of such a correspondence follows from the axiom of constructibility.

All these applications suggest of course the question whether the axiom of constructibility is true. The problem would of course be solved if it were possible to derive the axiom of constructibility from the other axioms of set theory. It was shown quite recently that no such derivation exists.

There exist therefore two mutually contradictory systems of set-theoretical axioms: one accepts the axiom of constructibility, the other rejects it. It is a highly pertinent question whether the choice between these two systems is just a matter of taste or whether there are compelling reasons to accept one of them as a basis for mathematics.

Gödel declared himself very strongly in favour of the set theory which rejects the axiom of constructibility, but his reasons are not quite clear [61]. The need to answer the fundamental philosophical question whether there are objective criteria of truth in mathematics has never been felt as strongly as in connection with the axiom of constructibility.

We mention still some formal results somewhat related to the question whether the axiom of constructibility is true or false. If the axiom is false, then there should exist formulae which are valid in the domain of constructible sets but invalid in the whole domain of sets. Shoenfield [207] discussed simple formulae of the form

$$(*) \quad \bigvee_X \bigwedge_n R\,(\overline{c_X(n)}) \qquad \bigwedge_X \bigvee_n R\,(\overline{c_X(n)}) \qquad (R \text{ is computable})$$

and of similar form with two set-quantifiers. He found that in the domain of these formulae there is no difference between constructible sets and arbitrary sets. If any of the formulae (*) is true in the domain of constructible sets of integers, it is also true in the domain of all sets of integers, and conversely. Formulae with three or more

set quantifiers do not behave in this way, however; there are formulae true in the domain of constructible sets but false in the domain
of all sets, provided that non-constructible sets exist.

The notion of constructibility introduced by Gödel has been
transformed in various ways, and these transformed notions can
be used for several purposes. An interesting modification has been
proposed by Cohen [23] who used it to obtain a minimal model for
the Zermelo—Fraenkel set theory.

Cohen takes as T_0 the empty set and defines the sets T_a by induction; if $C_a = \bigcup_{\beta < a} T_\beta$, then he includes in T_a all sets of the
following form:

(1) $\qquad\qquad \{x, y\}$ where $x, y \in C_a$,

(2) $\qquad\qquad \bigcup_{y \in x} y$ where $x \in C_a$,

(3) $\qquad \{y : (y \subset x) \wedge (y \in C_a)\}$ where $x \in C_a$,

(4) $\quad \{z : (z \in C_a) \wedge \bigvee_y [(y \in x) \wedge \models C_a F[y, z, u_1, \ldots, u_k]]\}$

where F is a first-order formula, $x, u_1, \ldots, u_k \in C_a$ and F satisfies
the condition that for every y in x there is exactly one z in C_a such
that $\models C_a F[y, z, u_1, \ldots, u_k]$.

He shows that there is a denumerable ordinal a such that $T_{a+1} = T_a$
and that T_a is a model for the Zermelo—Fraenkel set theory. This
model is minimal in the sense that it is contained in every transitive
family of sets in which all the axioms of set theory are satisfied.

From the existence of the minimal model Cohen drew the following
curious consequence which in the case of the Bernays—Gödel axioms
was noted already by Shepherdson [201]: There exists no formula R
such that one can prove in set theory that the elements x satisfying
$R(x)$ form a model for a set theory with the negation of the axiom
of constructibility.

The situation is completely different in the case of models satisfying the axiom of constructibility. There exists a formula (obtained
by formalizing the definition of a constructible set) such that it is
provable in set theory that the totality of elements satisfying this
formula is a model for set theory with the axiom of constructibility.
Hence we can obtain using this formula a proof of relative consistency of the axiom of constructibility. The result of Shepherdson
and Cohen shows that no such method is available if one wants to

prove the independence of the axiom of constructibility. Hence the independence problem is more difficult than the problem of consistency.

Let us still mention that Scott proposed other modifications of the notion of constructibility by allowing higher-order definitions in the construction of the set $D(K)$. Scott obtained in this way a very elegant new proof of the relative consistency of the axiom of choice.

Let us summarize the essential steps of our discussion. The problem of the consistency of set-theoretical hypotheses, such as the generalized continuum hypothesis, is a formal problem. The solution which Gödel gave to it was obtained by extending and modifying the nominalistic (predicative) approach to mathematics. There are close connections between the theory of hierarchies and the theory of constructible sets: the latter theory is an extension of the former into the Cantorian transfinite. The actual proof of the generalized continuum hypothesis from the axiom of constructibility uses also the Skolem — Löwenheim theorem and thus ties the theory of constructible sets with the theory of models.

The new axiom helps to solve various problems; yet it must be considered as a very dubious hypothesis. The problem of its independence proved to be very difficult.

Although the theory started with a formal problem, it touches the deep and fundamental problem of truth of set-theoretical hypotheses. We see no way of deciding the question whether the axiom of constructibility is true or false; what is worse, even an exact formulation of the problem does not seem to be possible.

All these facts are highly significant for everyone who is seriously interested in the mutual relations of mathematics and philosophy.

Lecture X

Various interpretations of the intuitionistic logic

We devote this lecture to a review of the interpretations proposed for intuitionistic logic and arithmetic. These interpretations are formulated in the language of classical logic; they were formulated not by intuitionists but by representatives of classical mathematics who wanted to make intuitionistic conceptions accessible to non-intuitionists.

By intuitionistic logic we mean here a predicate calculus without identity but with two quantifiers $\bigvee$, $\bigwedge$. We assume that an infinite number of constants $c_1, c_2, \ldots$ are available in the calculus. The logical axioms are those of the intuitionistic propositional logic plus the following two schemata for quantifiers:

$$\bigwedge_x Fx \to Fa \qquad Fa \to \bigvee_x Fx.$$

The rules of proof are the following: the *modus ponens* and the two rules

$$\frac{A \to Fx}{A \to \bigwedge_x Fx} \qquad \frac{Fx \to A}{\bigvee_x Fx \to A}$$

where A does not contain the free variable x.

In the intuitionistic arithmetic we assume that all formulae $F, G, \ldots$ are built by means of propositional connectives and quantifiers from equations between terms; terms in turn are built from constants and variables by means of symbols for arithmetical functions. Intuitionistic arithmetic is based on all the logical axioms and the usual axioms of Peano.

Topological and algebraic interpretations. This interpretation is a natural extension of the topological interpretation of the propositional calculus which we sketched in lecture I. The underlying idea is to choose an appropriate algebraic structure S as the set of truth-values. In the case of classical logic we choose as S the two-element Boolean algebra. In the case of intuitionistic logic we choose as S a (partially) ordered set which is complete in the sense that every non void subset $S_1 \subset S$ has the greatest lower bound (g.l.b.) and and the least upper bound (l.u.b.) in S. The g.l.b. of S_1 is the greatest element which stands in the relation $\leq$ to every element of S_1 and the l.u.b. of S_1 is the smallest element which stands in the relation $\geq$ to every element of S_1. These elements are denoted by $\bigwedge_{x \in S_1} x$ and $\bigvee_{x \in S_1} x$, respectively, or in case S_1 is a finite set $\{a, b, \ldots, m\}$ simply by $a \wedge b \wedge \ldots \wedge m$ and $a \vee b \vee \ldots \vee m$, respectively.

For arbitrary a, b in S we denote by $a \to b$ the l.u.b. of the elements x such that $a \wedge x \leq b$: $a \to b = \bigvee_{x \in S_1} x$ where $S_1 = \{x : a \wedge x \leq b\}$.

A model of intuitionistic logic over S is determined by a set $I \neq 0$ which we interpret as a range of individual variables. Predicates are interpreted as functions with arguments in I and values in S. A valuation is a mapping g of the set of all variables and constants into I and of the set of predicates with k arguments ($k = 0, 1, 2, \ldots$) into the set of functions with k arguments such that the arguments range over I and values over S. We define in the same way as in the classical case the value of a formula A for the valuation g (in symbols: $Val(A, g)$). The definition proceeds by induction: If A is an atomic formula $F(x_1, \ldots, x_k)$ where F is a k-place predicate and the x_i are variables or constants, then $Val(A, g) = f(g(x_1), \ldots, g(x_k))$ where f is the mapping of I^k into S correlated with F. If A is one of the formulae $B \vee C$, $B \wedge C$, $B \to C$, and $\neg B$, then $Val(A, g)$ is $Val(B, g) \vee Val(C, g)$, $Val(B, g) \wedge Val(C, g)$, $Val(B, g) \to Val(C, g)$, $Val(B, g) \to 0$, respectively. It should be noted here that the symbols $\wedge$, $\vee$, $\to$ between formulae denote propositional connectives and the same symbols between expressions $Val(B, g)$ and $Val(C, g)$ denote operations on elements of S; 0 denotes the minimal element of S, i.e. $\bigwedge_{x \in S} x$.

Finally we assume $Val(\bigwedge_x F, g) = \bigwedge_{i \in I} Val(F, g_i)$, $Val(\bigvee_x F, g) = \bigvee_{i \in I} Val(F, g_i)$, where g_i is a valuation which correlates the element i to the variable x and coincides on all other places with g.

This construction is an immediate generalization of the usual definition of satisfaction for classical logic. It is applicable with minor changes to other non-classical systems of logic, e.g. to the modal logics of Lewis and Langford. The first to give an explicit definition of the function *Val* for intuitionistic logic was Chandra-sekharan [13]; since then it has been widely used by various authors. A most comprehensive account of the subject is given in the recent book of Rasiowa and Sikorski [173].

It is easy to prove that for arbitrary S and $I \neq 0$ (satisfying the conditions specified above) we have $Val(F, g) = 1 (= O \to O)$ for all intuitionistically provable formulae F. This result is a basis for various independence proofs in the intuitionistic logic. We can show for instance that for some S, I and g we have $Val(F, g) \neq 1$ where F is the formula

$$\neg \bigwedge_x Hx \to \bigvee_x \neg Hx.$$

Hence this formula is not provable intuitionistically. The structure S used in this case as well as in many similar cases consists of open subsets of a topological space.

These independence proofs suggest the problem of completeness: Let X be a fixed topological space, let S be the family of its open subsets and let I be a fixed infinite set. Does the set of formulae which identically satisfy the equation $Val(F, g) = 1$ coincide with the set of intuitionistically provable formulae?

Rasiowa [171] solved the completeness problem by showing that there exists a space X satisfying these conditions. Sikorski [210] strengthened her result by proving that there exists a closed subset X of the Cantor discontinuous set which possesses the same property. For many spaces the question is still open.

The intuitionistic models of Beth. Beth [8] proposed another modification of the classical notion of a model and obtained in this way an adequate interpretation of intuitionistic logic. His construction was discussed by Kreisel and Dyson [29] who supplied various details omitted by Beth and corrected several minor inaccuracies.

Let F be a formula containing only the predicates $P_1, \ldots, P_k$. Beth defines his models by considering trees, *i.e.* figures consisting of points joined by oriented edges. It is assumed that there are only finitely many edges starting in a given point and that there is exactly one "initial" point which is reached by no edge. A branch consists of a finite or infinite sequence of edges such that the end-point of each edge is the beginning of the next. We assume that no branch forms a closed curve. A sub-tree of a given tree consists of points which can be reached from a given point p as well as from all points lying on the branch which connects the initial point with p. This sub-tree is said to be determined by p. A tree T is decomposed into sub-trees $T_{p_1}, \ldots, T_{p_n}$ if each infinite branch starting in the initial point passes through one of the points p_i.

Let now T be a tree and let us assume that with each point p there is correlated a finite sequence of formulae each containing no free variables and no predicate different from $P_1, \ldots, P_k$. These formulae are said to be connected with p.

The inductive definition of satisfaction is as follows: An atomic formula A is true on the tree T if T can be decomposed in a finite number of sub-trees $T_{p_1}, \ldots, T_{p_n}$ such that the formula A is connected with each p_i.

$\neg A$ is true on T if the formula A is true on T' for no sub-tree of T'.

$A \vee B$ is true on T if T can be decomposed in a finite number of trees such that on each of them either A or B is true.

$A \wedge B$ is true on T if A and B are true on T.

$A \to B$ is true on T if for every sub-tree T' of T it is the case that if A is true on T', then B is true on T'.

$\bigwedge_x Fx$ is true on T if Fc_n is true on T for each n.

$\bigvee_x Fx$ is true on T if T can be decomposed in a finite number of sub-trees $T_{p_1}, \ldots, T_{p_k}$ and if there exist k constants $c_{j_1}, \ldots, c_{j_k}$ such that each Fc_{j_i} is true on T_{p_i}.

The completeness theorem proved by Beth says that intuitionistically provable formulae coincide with formulae which are true on every tree.

Let us take as an example the formula $p \vee \neg p$ with an atomic p. The tree of diagram 5 (p. 94) shows that this formula is not an intuitionistic theorem. Indeed, it is easy to see that there is no decomposition of this tree in a finite number of sub-trees such that on each sub-tree either p or $\neg p$ be valid.

A related interpretation of intuitionistic logic was given by Lorenzen [124] who used the notion of a "dialogue".

There exists a close connection between the topological interpretation and Beth's construction. Each tree determines a topological space consisting of all its branches. In this space every point p determines a neighbourhood consisting of all branches going through p. We shall call this neighbourhood simply p.

Let us correlate with each predicate P_i (with, say, k arguments) the following function $f_i : f_i(a_1, \ldots, a_k)$ is the union of those neigh-

Diagram 5.

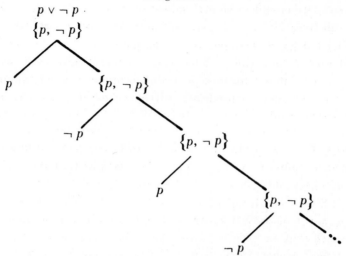

bourhoods p for which $P_i(c_{a_1}, \ldots, c_{a_k})$ is true on T_p. Take as I the set of integers and as S the ordered set of all open subsets of the space determined by the tree. To each P_i we have then correlated a mapping of I^k into S, and we have thus obtained a topological model of the sort discussed above. Kreisel and Dyson [29] showed that — under suitable assumptions — a formula is true on the tree if and only if its value in the corresponding topological model is 1. The assumption which we must make is that an atomic formula true on a sub-tree T' of T must be true on every sub-tree of T'.

Trees and topological models are very convenient in discussing pure logic.[1] Perhaps they could also be used for interpreting Brouwer's theory of "free choice sequences" and their species but no such applications have ever been made. It is less probable that interpretations of this kind can be found for intuitionistic arithmetic.

Realizability. Kleene [99][2] proposed an interpretation of intuitionistic arithmetic. Before describing the details of his construction we insert a few general remarks.

The purpose of an interpretation of a system is to give a precise meaning to notions which are either incompletely explained or taken as

---

[1] Kripke's paper [117a], which appeared when this book was in the press, contains further information about this subject.

[2] More recent exposition of this theory is given in [109a], pp. 90—132.

primitives in the system under consideration. In the case of predicate logic the notions to be interpreted are the connectives and the quantifiers. The intuitionists have given in their writings some explanations as to how they understand the connectives. We saw in lecture I that the fundamental notion to which all intuitionistic notions are reducible is that of a construction. This fundamental notion is only implicitly used by intuitionists. Kleene's proposal amounts to making the reduction explicit and moreover to identify constructions with partial computable functions. Since these functions can be enumerated we may formally identify a construction with an integer.

The interpretation of the universal quantifier proposed by Kleene is as follows: a construction whose number is e establishes the truth of the formula $\bigwedge_x Ax$ if the partial computable function f whose number is e has the property that for each n the integer $f(n)$ is the number of a construction which establishes the truth of $A(\bar{n})$. The meaning of an existential formula $\bigvee_x Ax$ is similar. A construction whose number is e establishes the truth of this formula if we can read off from e an integer n and a number e' such that e' is the number of a construction which establishes $A(\bar{n})$.

The details of Kleene's interpretation are as follows: let $K(e)$ and $L(e)$ be two functions such that the mapping $e \rightleftarrows (Ke, Le)$ establishes a one-one correspondence between integers and pairs of integers. Let F be a partial computable function such that $F(0, x), F(1, x), \ldots$ is an enumeration of all partial computable functions. We shall write $F_e(x)$ instead of $F(e, x)$. With these notations we are going to define a relation "e realizes A", where A is an arithmetical formula without free variables.

Case 1. A is an atomic formula; in this case e realizes A if and only if A is true. We use of course the fact that primitive arithmetical predicates are all decidable and that the truth and falsity of an atomic formula is therefore a well-defined notion.

Case 2. A is the formula $B \wedge C$. In this case e realizes A if and only if $K(e)$ realizes B and $L(e)$ realizes C.

Case 3. A is the formula $B \vee C$. In this case e realizes A if and only if either $L(e) = 0$ and $K(e)$ realizes B or $L(e) = 1$ and $K(e)$ realizes C.

Case 4. A is the formula $B \rightarrow C$. In this case e realizes A if and only if for each n either n does not realize B or $F_e(n)$ exists and realizes C.

Case 5. A is the formula $\neg B$. This case is reducible to the previous one because $\neg B$ is the same as $B \to 0 \neq 0$.

Case 6. A is the formula $\bigwedge_x B(x)$. In this case e realizes A if and only if for each n the number $F_e(n)$ exists and realizes $B(\bar{n})$.

Case 7. A is the formula $\bigvee_x B(x)$. In this case e realizes A if and only if $K(e)$ realizes $B(\overline{L(e)})$.

The relation "e realizes A" is thus defined. Kleene has shown that all formulae which are provable in intuitionistic arithmetic are realizable by an arbitrary e. The hypothesis that only such formulae have this property has been disproved by Rose [186].

Kleene's notion of realizability hence does not give us an adequate interpretation. This shows that the identification of constructions with computable partial functions is unjustified: There must exist intuitionistically acceptable "constructions" which are not reducible to such functions.

Gödel's interpretation by means of functionals. The principle of this interpretation which was proposed by Gödel in [62] is similar to that of the realizability interpretation but the class of admissible constructions is much wider. These constructions are identified not with functions but with functionals.

In order to see how the functionals appear in the interpretations of formulae let us consider an example. Let A be the formula $\neg \bigwedge_x \bigvee_y Bxy$ where x and y are numerical variables. Using the idea of the no-counter-example interpretation (*cf.* lecture IV) we interpret this formula in the following way: Whichever function f we choose there exists a counter-example to the formula $\bigwedge_x B(x, f(x))$. In other words, there exists a functional Φ of type $((* : *) : *)$ such that we have $\neg F(\Phi(f), f(\Phi(f)))$. The interpretation of the formula $\neg \bigwedge_x \bigvee_y Fxy$ is thus the formula $\bigvee_\Phi \bigwedge_f \neg F(\Phi(f), f(\Phi(f)))$.

Gödel defines for every arithmetical formula F (with or without free variables) its translation F^*; the translation has always the same free variables as F and has the form $\bigvee_p \bigwedge_q F'(p, q)$ where p and q are finite sequences of variables whose values are functionals. The exact definition of the translation is inductive:

If A is an atomic formula, then $A^* = A' = A$;

If A is the formula $B \wedge C$, then A^* is the formula

$$\bigvee_{p_1, p_2} \bigwedge_{q_1, q_2} [B'(p_1, q_1) \wedge C'(p_2, q_2)];$$

If A is the formula $B \vee C$, then $A*$ is the formula

$$\bigvee_{r, p_1, p_2} \bigwedge_{q_1, q_2} \{[(r = 0) \wedge B'(p_1, q_1)] \vee [(r = 1) \vee C'(p_2, q_2)]\};$$

If A is the formula $B \to C$, then $A*$ is the formula [1]

$$\bigvee_{\Phi, \Psi} \bigwedge_{p_1, q_2} [B'(p_1, \Psi(p_1, q_2)) \to C'(\Phi(p_1), q_2)];$$

(The case when A is $\neg B$ is reducible to the former ones since $\neg B$ is equivalent to $B \to (0 \neq 0)$);

If A is the formula $\bigvee_x B(x)$, then $A*$ is the formula

$$\bigvee_{x, p} \bigwedge_q B'(x, p, q);$$

If A is the formula $\bigwedge_x B(x)$, then $A*$ is the formula

$$\bigvee_{\Phi} \bigwedge_{x, q} B'(\Phi(x), q).$$

The most complicated rule for implication is explained by Gödel as follows: We have to correlate with every *example* of a p_1 satisfying the condition $\bigwedge_{q_1} B'(p_1, q_1)$ an example $p_2 = \Phi(p_1)$ satisfying $\bigwedge_{q_2} C'(\Phi(p_1), q_2)$ and with every *counter-example* q_2 satisfying $\neg C'(\Phi(p_1), q_2)$ a counter-example $q_1 = \Psi(p_1, q_2)$ satisfying $\neg B'(p_1, q_1)$.

The definition of $F*$ thus completed, Gödel limits the variability of functionals to the class of primitive recursive functionals. Translations of all formulae provable in the intuitionistic arithmetic become then intuitively true statements concerning these functionals. Moreover, these statements are provable in the axiomatic theory T of primitive recursive functionals which we mentioned in lecture VIII. This shows the consistency of the intuitionistic (and hence of the classical) arithmetic relative to T.

It is not known whether the property of having the translation provable in T is characteristic for intuitionistically provable arithmetical theorems.

---

[1] In this formula Φ and Ψ are finite sequences of variables. If *e.g.* Φ consists of $\varphi, \psi, \ldots$, then $\Phi(p)$ denotes the sequence $\varphi(p), \psi(p), \ldots$ and similarly in other cases.

7

An extension of Gödel's ideas to second-order arithmetic has been carried out by Spector [216].

All the interpretations we have discussed in this lecture try to explain intuitionistic notions in classical terms. An intuitionist might ask: How can one explain these classical notions in intuitionistic terms? This problem, which is accessible only to intuitionists or people who can think in terms of the intuitionistic logic, has been discussed by Kreisel [113].

It seems to me that the study of mutual interpretations of the classical and intuitionistic systems is extremely useful. By developing them we can hope to reach at least a partial understanding between these two schools.

Lecture XI

Constructive foundations of mathematics

After the discovery of set-theoretical antinomies several mathematicians decided that the only radical solution of the problem raised by these antinomies is to exclude all general set-theoretical notions from mathematics and to limit oneself to the study of those objects that can be effectively defined or constructed. We have already discussed the ideas of the intuitionists and seen that the limitation to constructible objects is an essential feature of their program. There are several other constructive trends less extreme than intuitionism; their program is to limit the domain of admissible mathematical objects to a more or less arbitrarily chosen class without challenging (as the intuitionists do) the classical rules of proof. Since the class of admissible objects is not uniquely determined we cannot speak of a unique constructive trend; there are, on the contrary, many mutually conflicting constructive programs which differ from each other in many details, sometimes important ones, although their general tendencies are similar.

We shall first discuss works whose aim is to examine constructive objects by quite arbitrary means. Since these means are not necessarily admissible from the constructive point of view, it is clear that the results obtained in this way cannot claim philosophical importance. They are sometimes interesting from a purely mathematical point of view, however.

Computable analysis. This theory restricts all mathematical notions and in particular those which occur in mathematical analysis to computable functions. The notion of integer is taken over from classical arithmetic and not analyzed any further. The notion of a real number and all other mathematical notions undergo limitations which aim at an elimination of all non-computable notions.

Specker [211] considered a very narrow class of real numbers which he called primitive recursive. These numbers can be approximated with the accuracy $(^1/_2)^n$ by fractions which have the form $[f'(n) - f''(n)] / g(n)$ where f', f'', g are primitive recursive functions:

(*) $| \alpha - [f'(n) - f''(n)] / g(n) | < (^1/_2)^n.$

He also considered various other types of approximations, *e.g.*
by partial sums of the series $\Sigma f(n) / g^n$ where f is a primitive recursive
function which satisfies the condition $f(n) < g$ for all n. Still other
approximations make use of the notion of a primitive recursive
cut. Specker discovered various singularities in the behaviour of
these numbers. He proved for instance that a number α may have
a primitive recursive decimal expansion whereas 3α fails to have
such an expansion. Specker's work was continued among others by
Péter [159].

A more comprehensive class consists of the numbers known as
computable real numbers. These numbers satisfy for each n the
inequality (*) in which f', f'', g are computable functions. They were
defined by various authors (Rice [174], Robinson [178], Mazur [141])
who showed that the singularities discovered by Specker in case of primitive recursive numbers do not hold for computable numbers. They
proved *e.g.* that a real number α is computable if and only if the
sequence of digits in its decimal expansion is computable.

One proves easily that computable numbers form a real closed
field. Hence the usual algebraic operations can be performed on
computable numbers and yield computable results.

In order to develop further parts of analysis one introduces computable sequences and computable functions of a real variable.

A sequence $\{\alpha_m\}$ of real numbers is computable if there exist computable functions f, f', g of two variables such that the following
inequality holds for arbitrary m and n:

$$| \alpha_m - [f(m, n) - f'(m, n)] / g(m, n) | < (^1/_2)^n.$$

In other words, we require that for each n and m we can fix (in
a computable way) an interval of length $(^1/_2)^n$ which contains α_m.
There is of course a certain degree of arbitrariness in this definition.
Instead of using an approximation by rationals we could start from
any other means of appproximation, *e.g.* we could require that the
n-th decimal digit in the expansion of α_m be given by a computable
function of m and n. There are several rather difficult arithmetical
questions which arise in connection with these definitions, for instance:

Is there a computable sequence $\{a_m\}$ such that the sequence of the digits of the expansion $a_m = \Sigma f(m, n, g) \,/\, g^n$ is computable for no g? Questions of this kind only quite recently have received answers (*cf.* Lachlan [119]).

Computable sequences of reals do not have all the properties one would like them to have. Mazur showed, for example, that there is a computable sequence a_m with all terms different from 0 such that the sequence $1/a_m$ is not computable.

The most important and at the same time the most difficult notion is that of a computable function of a real variable. We shall limit ourselves to functions of a non-negative variable with non-negative real values.

To each such function φ we associate a functional Φ as follows: Let α be approximated by a fraction $f(n) \,/\, 2^n$: $|\, \alpha - f(n) \,/\, 2^n \,| < (^1/_2)^n$. We find a similar approximation of $\beta_n = \varphi(f(n) \,/\, 2^n)$:

$$|\, \beta_n - g(n, m) \,/\, 2^m \,| < (^1/_2)^m$$

Thus $g(n, m)$ is the value of a functional $\Phi(f, n, m)$ whose type is $(((* : *), *, *): *)$; this functional allows us to find an approximation of $\varphi(\alpha)$ for a given approximation of α. Most definitions of computable real functions make use of this functional Φ.

Banach and Mazur [141] called a function φ computable if it carries any computable sequence a_n again into a computable sequence. The corresponding functional Φ carries then each function $\lambda x \, f(n, x)$ (where f is a computable function) into a computable function.

Functionals with this property are called Banach—Mazur functionals. Such a functional remains a Banach-Mazur functional after arbitrary changes of its values at non-computable arguments. Hence there is no point to consider the Banach—Mazur functionals for non-computable values of arguments.

The Banach—Mazur real functions are continuous at every computable point. Mazur established various other properties of these functions, *e.g.* the so called property of Darboux which says that if $\varphi(\alpha) < 0$, $\varphi(\beta) > 0$ where α and β are computable and $\alpha < \beta$, then there is a computable γ such that $\alpha < \gamma < \beta$ and $\varphi(\gamma) = 0$.

The class of Banach—Mazur functions and functionals is rather wide. Several narrower classes of functions were investigated by various authors. Thus *e.g.* Myhill and Shepherdson [155] and later

Kreisel—Lacombe—Shoenfield [116] considered partial recursive functionals. If F_0, F_1, ... is a standard enumeration of partial computable functions and f a fixed partial computable function then the functional $\Phi(F_e) = f(e)$ is a partial recursive functional. Thus the domain of such a functional consists of partial recursive functions and the computation of its value consists of a computation performed on a number e which the argument has in the standard enumeration. We have to assume that f is chosen so that if $F_e = F_e'$ then $f(e) = f(e')$. Partial recursive functionals give rise to a class of real functions, called partial recursive.

Another possibility is to admit partial computable functionals. These functionals correlate with each function f a partial function computable relative to f (cf. lecture VII). We shall call them the Kleene functionals. The range of the arguments of a full Kleene functional consists of all functions not only of computable ones. Hence the corresponding real functions are insofar different from the Banach—Mazur functions as they are defined everywhere and not only for computable values of the arguments.

Still another class of functionals was proposed by Grzegorczyk [66] who defined it as the smallest class closed under some operations among whom the operation of effective minimum was the most characteristic. Kleene [106] called these functionals μ-recursive but we prefer the name Grzegorczyk-functionals.

We have thus four notions of functionals and of real functions: Banach—Mazur functionals, partial recursive functionals, Kleene functionals and Grzegorczyk functionals. The mutual relations of these various classes were discussed in several papers.

Friedberg [45] showed that Banach—Mazur functionals form an essentially wider class than partial recursive functionals; this result is very deep. Myhill and Shepherdson [155] proved a much easier result that every partial recursive functional can be extended to a Kleene functional. Kreisel—Lacombe—Shoenfield [116] sharpened this result by showing that the same property is also possessed by functionals defined only on total computable functions.

From standard results on computable functions and functionals (cf. Kleene [104]) it follows that Grzegorczyk functionals coincide with total Kleene functionals.

It follows from these results that positive theorems (i.e. theorems stating that each functional has a property) valid for the Banach—Mazur class are true for all other classes. Thus all real functions corresponding to partial recursive, partial computable and μ-recursive functionals are continuous and possess the property of Darboux.

Grzegorczyk showed that his functionals and hence the corresponding real functions are uniformly continuous. Lacombe [120] (*cf.* also Specker [212]) showed that real functions of Grzegorczyk not always attain the maximum in a computable point. This negative result severely restricts the possibility of repeating classical proofs in the computable analysis. Such reconstructions were attempted in various papers, for instance in Klaua [96].

A very specific notion of a real function was proposed also by Brouwer. His definition makes use of terms and notions accessible only to intuitionists. Kleene [102] has shown that one obtains a persuasive interpretation if one explains these notions in terms of partial computable functionals. Under his interpretation free choice sequences of Brouwer are simply arbitrary sequences; Brouwer's "functions" are partial computable functionals. Assuming that this interpretation represents faithfully the intuitionistic notions we come to the conclusion that Brouwer's ideas on foundations of analysis were pretty far from constructive ideas in the orthodox constructivism which does not accept arbitrary sequences of integers.

Another branch of computable mathematics is the theory of recursive equivalence of sets of integers created and developed by Dekker and Myhill [27]. This theory examines notions obtained from set-theoretical ones by replacing arbitrary sets by sets of integers and arbitrary mappings of sets by partial recursive ones.

Extensions of computable mathematics. In computable mathematics we reduce all notions to computable ones. Various authors examined other possibilities. Thus *e.g.* Grzegorczyk [67] studied a system which he called the "elementarily definable analysis". In this system all notions are reduced to such as can be defined in terms of integers and their first-order theory. It was Weyl who already in the early twenties developed such a theory for the first time, of course without using the much more modern notion of definability.

Another possibility is to use the class of hyper-arithmetic sets and functions although it is a debatable question whether a theory based on these notions can claim to be constructive.

Some results in hyper-arithmetic analysis were obtained by Kreisel [115] who investigated the possibility of proving in it an analogue of the classical Cantor—Bendixon theorem.

Whatever the mathematical interest of such theories may be it is certain that strictly finitistic theories are much more satisfactory from the philosophical point of view.

Strictly finitistic theories. By strictly finitistic we mean theories which limit not only the class of objects but also the class of admissible methods of proof. According to this terminology even the computable analysis as described above is not strictly finitistic since it operates with classical mathematical notions without restriction and takes no care which laws of logic are used. Even the notion of computable function is not unobjectionable from the strictly finitistic point of view because in all definitions of this notion occur some clauses which cannot be verified in a finite number of steps.

Strictly finitistic attitude was represented since long by Skolem who formulated the concept of recursive arithmetic. His idea was taken up by Goodstein in two books [63], [64] published in 1957 and 1961. The main idea of recursive arithmetic is to develop mathematics as a formal system which operates exclusively with equations. The number of functional constants is not limited, new constants being added either by explicit or inductive definitions. The rules of proof are just the rule of substitution (of terms for variables throughout a proven equation), the rule of "replacing equals by equals"

$$\frac{F = G}{A(F) = A(G)}$$

and a rule which says that $F = G$ whenever both F and G satisfy equations of a recursive definition.

There are no quantifiers in this theory nor are there propositional connectives. We do not assume, in recursive arithmetic the existence of a set of all integers. Also it is irrelevant for this system which kind of logic do we admit since no logical notions occur in it.

Several theorems of analysis can be proved in recursive arithmetic. This is true for theorems expressible by means of approximations of real numbers by rational numbers. For instance if f is a real function and if we can define a primitive recursive operation which from an approximation of x by means of a rational number produces a rational approximation of $f(x)$, then this operation can be taken as a definition of a sort of the function f. Goodstein succeeded to establish a series of theorems which are analogues in recursive arithmetic of the classical theorems of analysis.

The idea of recursive arithmetic found a rather unexpected application. Church [21] constructed a system very similar to this arithmetic in which arithmetical operations are replaced by Boolean ones and applied it to a description of electric circuits with retarding elements.

Another extremely consistent system of constructive mathematics was created by Markov and his collaborators. The basic notion to which all other notions are reduced by the representatives of this school is the notion of an algorithm. In Markov's school all definitions are expressed in everyday language and all references to actual infinity are strictly avoided. Although Markov and his followers consciously refrain from formulating the logic which they admit, it is clear that they accept the intuitionistic logic. Thus we see that there are essential differences between Markov's conceptions and recursive arithmetic: the former school accepts all algorithms, the latter only those which correspond to primitive recursive functions; the former uses (informally) the intuitionistic logic, the latter avoids using logic altogether.

Real numbers and their sequences are defined in Markov's theory as in computable analysis, the only difference being that numbers are replaced everywhere by algorithms which define their successive approximations. One consequence of this is that the relation of identity (for real numbers) is no more decidable, since there is no algorithm which would allow us to decide whether any two given algorithms define approximations of one and the same real number.

The notion of a real function is again defined by Markov with the help of algorithms. He identifies a real function with an algorithm which correlates with each algorithm A another algorithm A' in such a way that if A and A_1 define two approximations to one and the same real number then so do A' and A_1'. We thus see that Markov chose for his real functions the notion equivalent to that of a partial computable functional.

Markov's theory is exposed in [139]. His work was continued by Šanin [192] who investigated analogues of various classical theories in the constructive mathematics of Markov.

He was able to develop even as advanced parts of analysis as the theories of Hilbert space and Lebesgue integral. Because of constructivistic limitations these theories do not behave as their classical models and are usually much less elegant. Šanin [191] found for instance that in the constructive theory of the Lebesgue integral it is not permissible in general to interchange the operation of integration with that of a passage to a limit. Yet it was precisely to obtain this theorem that Lebesgue formulated his definition of the integral!

Personally I do not believe that it is worth-while to reconstruct classical theories in constructive terms. No particularly interesting results have been obtained, and hardly anybody believes that the cumbersome theories obtained in this way will really replace the elegant classical theories. I am inclined to believe that there are branches of mathematics which simply are not susceptible to finitistic treatment.

There are of course branches of mathematics which can be treated in a finitistic way. Abstract algebra is an excellent example of such a domain. Methods and results of the recursive function theory can lead and have in fact led to many important and interesting results in this theory. We are often dealing in algebra with problems of pronounced algorithmic character; for instance, all questions concerning elementary transformations of polynomials taught in school belong to this group. Van der Waerden [240] and in a broader context Shepherdson and Fröhlich [47] discussed the problem which questions of the elementary theory of fields can be answered by using algorithms. To this end they considered fields whose operations are defined by means of computable functions. Thus they used the same device which is constantly used in computable arithmetic and analysis though with a completely different aim in mind. Further work along the same lines was also done by Rabin [168] and the general setting of the problem was given by Malcev [136]. Malcev did not limit himself to special systems like fields but considered arbitrary abstract algebras and the numerations of their elements such as to represent the basic operations of the algebra by means of computable functions. Although the aims which these authors pursue are incomparably more modest than the reconstruction of mathematics in the finitistic theories it is probable that the results of their works will last longer than the more ambitious but less fruitful conceptions of the finitistic school.

Lecture XII

Decision problems

The decision problem as formulated by Hilbert consists in finding criteria which would allow us to check in a finite number of steps whether any given formula of the first-order logic is or is not provable. In the period 1930—1964 this general problem was given an essentially negative answer, *i.e.* it was shown that no such criteria exist. Several partial problems nevertheless admit positive solutions; these positive solutions have found various applications.

Positive results. Let us first discuss a type of problem which was formulated already in Hilbert's school. We consider the semantically defined property of satisfiability of first-order formulae in some domain and ask whether there are criteria which allow us to decide effectively when a formula has this property. It has been shown that such criteria exist for certain classes of formulae.

Let F be a formula in which exactly one predicate P occur. Let us assume that P is binary and that F has the form $\bigvee_x \bigwedge_y M(x, y)$, where M contains no quantifiers, and let H_n be its n-th Herbrand disjunction:

$$H_n : M(x_1, x_2) \lor M(x_2, x_3) \lor \ldots \lor M(x_{n-1}, x_n).$$

We know from lecture V that F is provable if and only if there is an n such that H_n is provable.

This is evidently the case when H_2 is provable in the propositional calculus. We shall show that if H_2 is not provable in the propositional calculus, then no H_n can be provable in it. Indeed, there are the following atomic formulae in $M(x_1, x_2)$:

(i) $\qquad P(x_1, x_1), P(x_1, x_2), P(x_2, x_1), P(x_2, x_2)$

and hence the following formulae in $M(x_p, x_{p+1})$:

(ii)　　$P(x_p, x_p)$, $P(x_p, x_{p+1})$, $P(x_{p+1}, x_p)$, $P(x_{p+1}, x_{p+1})$.

According to our assumption we can assign truth-values t_{11}, t_{12}, t_{21}, t_{22} to the atomic formulae (i) in such a way that M becomes false. Two cases are now possible:

(A) the truth-values t_{ij} can be chosen so that $t_{11} = t_{22}$. In this case we can assign the truth-values t_{11}, t_{12}, t_{21}, t_{22} to the atomic formulae (ii) for $p = 2, 3, \ldots$. These assignments are consistent with each other and give the truth-value "false" to $M(x_p, x_{p+1})$. Hence H_n is not a theorem.

(B) $t_{11} \neq t_{22}$ for every assignment of truth-values t_{ij} to the formulae (i) which make $M(x_1, x_2)$ false. In this case we use the assumption that H_2 is not a theorem and infer that there is an assignment of truth-values t_{ij} to the atomic formulae

(iii)　　$P(x_1, x_1)$, $P(x_1, x_2)$, $P(x_2, x_1)$, $P(x_2, x_2)$, $P(x_2, x_3)$,

$$P(x_3, x_2), \ P(x_3, x_3)$$

which makes H_2 false. In this assignment $t_{11} = t_{33}$. Otherwise we would have $t_{22} = t_{33}$ (since $t_{11} \neq t_{22}$ by the definition of Case B), and by substituting x_1 for x_2 and x_2 for x_3 we would obtain an assignment t_{22}, t_{23}, t_{32}, t_{33} of truth-values to the atomic formulae (i) which makes $M(x_1, x_2)$ false and has the property that $P(x_1, x_1)$ and $P(x_2, x_2)$ are assigned the same truth-value. This would contradict the definition of Case B. Hence $t_{11} = t_{33}$, and we see that we can assign to the atomic formulae

$$P(x_{2p+1}, x_{2p+1}), \ P(x_{2p+1}, x_{2p+2}), \ P(x_{2p+2}, x_{2p+1}), \ P(x_{2p+2}, x_{2p+2}),$$
$$P(x_{2p+2}, x_{2p+3}), \ P(x_{2p+3}, x_{2p+2}), \ P(x_{2p+3}, x_{2p+3})$$

the same truth-values as to the formulae (iii) and that these assignments are consistent. Thus H_n is provable for no n. In this way we obtain a solution of the decision problem for the class of formulae we are considering. This solution was first given by Bernays and Schoenfinkel in 1928.

Similar combinatorial arguments can be applied to more complicated classes of formulae. The strongest result in this direction is due to Gödel [55] who solved the decision problem for first-order formulae of the form $\bigwedge\limits_{x_1 \ldots x_k} \bigvee\limits_{yz} \bigwedge\limits_{t_1 \ldots t_l} M$, where M has no quantifiers.

Another rather general result is due to Herbrand [79] who solved the decision problem for formulae with an arbitrary arrangement of initial quantifiers followed by a matrix in which the only connectives are disjunction and negation.

Herbrand's theorem discussed in lecture V provides a unifying principle for proofs of this sort.

A different type of a decision problem originated with Skolem [208]; it was developed mainly by Tarski in a number of papers of which the most important is [226]. The general character of these problems can be described as follows: Let us consider an axiomatic theory T based on the first-order logic. We ask for criteria for a given formula F to be provable in T. This is the decision problem for the theory T. If the general decision problem were solvable, then so would be the decision problem for every finitely axiomatizable theory T. Indeed, if $A_1, \ldots, A_n$ are all the axioms of T, then F is provable in T if and only if the formula $A_1 \wedge \ldots \wedge A_n \to F$ is provable in (pure) logic. Hence the decision problem for T is reduced to that for logic. This remark, interesting though it is, does not help us very much since the decision problem for logic is not solvable; moreover, the implication formulae just mentioned are not usually reducible to any of the forms for which the decision problem has been solved.

The method devised by Skolem and developed by Tarski is called the method of elimination. The scheme of this method is as follows: Let T be a first-order theory and

$$(1) \qquad P_i, \; P_i'(x), \; P_i''(x, y), \; P_i'''(x, y, z), \ldots \; (i = 0, 1, \ldots)$$

a sequence of formulae with $0, 1, 2, \ldots$ free variables. The number of these formulae may be finite or infinite. Let us assume that (i) each formula W of T is equivalent to a Boolean combination C of formulae (1) and that C can be found effectively for any given W. Let us assume, furthermore, that (ii) if W has at most n free variables, then C is built from those formulae (1) that have at most n free variables. Under these assumptions each W without free variables is equivalent to a Boolean combination of the formulae P_1, $P_2, \ldots$. Hence if we can decide when a Boolean combination of these formulae is provable in T we can decide when an arbitrary formula W is provable.

Assumptions (i) and (ii) are satisfied if formulae (1) satisfy the following conditions: (iii) each atomic formula of T occurs among the formulae (1); (iv) if K is a conjunction of formulae (1) and of their negations, then the formula $W = \bigvee_x K$ is equivalent to a Boolean combination of formulae (1) built from those formulae whose free variables occur in W.

The reduction of conditions (i) and (ii) to (iii), (iv) is based on a simple reduction of formulae to a standard form known as the prenex normal form.

The essential property of formulae (1) is (iv). It can be expressed by saying that a necessary and sufficient condition for the existence of an x satisfying K is expressible as a Boolean combination of formulae (1). The name "method of elimination" is borrowed from algebra where we often eliminate an unknown and express by certain equations and inequalities the necessary and sufficient condition for the solvability of an equation.

Let us illustrate the method on a simple example. Let us take as T the theory whose unique non-logical primitive notion is a binary relation R (the identity relation is treated as a logical notion). The axioms of the theory state that the universe is ordered by R and that every element has a predecessor and a successor:

$$Rxx, \quad Rxy \wedge Ryx \to x = y, \quad Rxy \wedge Ryz \to Rxz,$$

$$Rxy \vee x = y \vee Ryx,$$

$$\bigwedge_x \bigvee_{yz} (Rxy \wedge Rzx \wedge \bigwedge_s \{[Rxs \wedge x \neq s \to Rys] \wedge [Rsx \wedge s \neq x \to Rsz]\}.$$

We take as P_0 the formula $\bigwedge_x (x = x)$ and as $P_n(x, y)$ the formula

$$Rxy \wedge \bigvee_{x_1 \ldots x_{n+2}} \bigwedge_{0 < i < j \leq n+2} [(x_i \neq x_j) \wedge Rx_i x_j \wedge (x = x_1) \wedge (x_{n+2} = y)]$$

$$(n = 0, 1, 2, \ldots).$$

The formula $P_n(x,y)$ says that x precedes y and that there are at least n elements between x and y. It can be shown without much trouble that conditions (iii) and (iv) are satisfied in this example. Hence for each formula W without free variables we can find an equivalent Boolean combination of P_0 alone, whence it follows that the decision problem for T is solvable.

The elimination method was successfully used to solve the decision problem for various theories. The strongest result is due to Tarski [226] who established the decidability of the theory of real closed fields. Axioms of this theory consist of two groups. Axioms of the first group state that the universe of the theory is an ordered field; the number of these axioms is finite. Axioms of the second group form an infinite sequence and state that each equation of degree $3, 5, 7, \ldots$ has at least one root. (If we could define in the theory the general notion of a polynomial of an odd degree, we could replace this infinite sequence of axioms by a single sentence; however, this general notion is not definable.)

Another important example of a decidable theory is the theory of Abelian groups whose decidability has been proved by Szmielew [220]. This theory is of course incomplete; one can even show that it admits $2^{\aleph_0}$ complete extensions. The elimination method is, as we see, applicable to essentially different kinds of theories.

At the present moment the applications of the elimination method seem to be exhausted. With the exception of relatively simple cases familiar in the existing literature, the method leads to forbidding calculations which can hardly be undertaken by anybody. In the last few years new methods have appeared which have made it possible to solve the decision problem for several theories.

One of these new methods rests on the simple remark that complete theories based on a recursively enumerable set of axioms are always decidable. Since various methods of establishing the completeness of theories are known at present, we can in this way obtain solutions of the decision problem for complete theories. We shall say more about such proofs in lecture XIII.

Büchi [10], [11] used the theory of finite automata to obtain a solution of the decision problem of some fragments of the second-order arithmetic. The constants of this theory are 0 (zero) and ' (successor); there are two types of variables: lower case variables for integers and upper case variables for sets of integers.[1] According to whether we admit arbitrary sets or only finite sets as values of the set variables we distinguish the strong and the weak second-order arithmetic.

Both the weak and the strong second-order arithmetic are interpreted systems. The notions of truth, definability *etc.* in these systems are thus understood in the semantical sense.

In what follows we shall give an account of the work of Büchi concerned with the weak theory.

---

[1] We shall often identify a set with its characteristic function.

Büchi showed that each formula of the weak second-order arithmetic (without free variables) is equivalent to a formula of the form

$$(2) \quad \bigvee_{Y_1,\ldots,Y_n} [K(Y_1(0), \ldots, Y_n(0)) \wedge \bigwedge_t B(Y_1(t), \ldots, Y_n(t),$$
$$Y_1(t'), \ldots, Y_n(t'))]$$

where K and B contain but propositional connectives.

The truth of formula (2) can easily be checked. Let us assume for instance that $n = 1$ and that $B(\mathfrak{F}, \mathfrak{F})$ is true (where $\mathfrak{F}$ is the truth-value "false"). Since Y_1 has to be a finite set, formula (2) is true if and only if there exists a finite sequence $c_0, c_1, \ldots, c_{p-1} = \mathfrak{F}$ of truth-values such that $K(c_0)$ and $B(c_j, c_{j+1})$ are true for each $j < p$. The terms of this sequence are simply the truth-values of $Y_1(j)$, and p is the least integer such that no $q \geq p - 1$ is an element of Y_1. If there are two identical consecutive terms in the sequence $c_0, \ldots, c_{p-1}$ we can drop one of them without altering the properties of the sequence. Furthermore, the sequence $\mathfrak{F}\mathfrak{B}\mathfrak{F}\mathfrak{B}$ can be replaced by $\mathfrak{F}\mathfrak{B}$ and the sequence $\mathfrak{B}\mathfrak{F}\mathfrak{B}\mathfrak{F}$ by $\mathfrak{B}\mathfrak{F}$. Thus we see that it is sufficient to check whether the sequences $\mathfrak{F}$, $\mathfrak{F}\mathfrak{B}\mathfrak{F}$, $\mathfrak{B}\mathfrak{F}$ satisfy the conditions imposed on $c_0, \ldots, c_{p-1}$ and this can obviously be done in a finite number of steps.

The reduction to the form (2) is far from obvious. Büchi obtained it by using certain concepts from the theory of finite automata. Let us define this notion:

A finite automaton is determined by (i) its initial configuration, (ii) its transition functions, and (iii) its output function. The initial configuration is a string $E_1, \ldots, E_m$ of truth-values. The transition functions are propositional formulae $H_j(p_1, \ldots, p_m; q_1, \ldots, q_n)$ where $j = 1, 2, \ldots, m$. The output function is a propositional formula $U(p_1, \ldots, p_m)$. The functioning of an automaton can be described as follows: We first fix arbitrarily the values of the parameters $q_1, \ldots, q_n$ in the transition functions by giving them values $X_1, \ldots, X_n$, where each X_s is a function of t ultimately equal $\mathfrak{F}$. At each moment t the automaton is in a "stage" described by a string $r_1(t), \ldots, r_m(t)$ of truth-values. These "stage functions" are defined by induction:

$$r_k(0) = E_k, \quad r_k(t') = H_k(r_1(t), \ldots, r_m(t), X_1(t), \ldots, X_n(t)).$$

The output of the automaton at the moment t is defined as $u(t) = U(r_1(t), \ldots, r_m(t))$.

Thus an automaton presents us (for every choice of the parameters $X_1, \ldots, X_n$) with an infinite sequence $u(t)$ of truth-values. The set of values of the parameters for which the terms of this sequence are ultimately $\mathfrak{B}$ is called by Büchi the "behaviour" of the automaton. The main result of Büchi obtained by analyzing the formulae of the weak second-order arithmetic is that each set S of n-tuples $X_1, \ldots, X_n$ (where each X_s is a function of t ultimately equal $\mathfrak{F}$) which is definable in the weak second-order arithmetic is the behaviour of a finite automaton, and conversely.

Since the behaviour of an automaton can be described by a formula of form (2), the desired reduction of formulae to form (2) follows.

The principle of Büchi's result for the strong second-order arithmetic is similar, but the reduction to form (2) is much more involved, chiefly because we cannot assume that the functions X_s are ulti-mately equal $\mathfrak{F}$.

Let us mention here that the recursive arithmetic of Church [21] coincides with the formal theory of finite automata in Büchi's sense.

Negative results. The basic method used in proofs of undecidability is the reduction of the decision problem for a class K to the decision problem of another class K_0 for which the solution of the decision problem is known to be negative. It is obvious that if the characteristic function of K_0 is computable relative to the characteristic function of K and if the former function is not computable, then the latter is not computable, either. Hence the set K is not computable. Identifying the (intuitive) notion of decidability with the (formal) notion of computability, we obtain in this way a negative solution of the decision problem for the set K. In lectures IV and VII we gave several examples of sets whose characteristic functions are not computable. By means of the reduction procedure it is possible to obtain various proofs of undecidability. We shall mention a few of them.

The first result of this kind is due to Church [17] who proved the undecidability of the full predicate logic, thus solving Hilbert's original problem. Church's result showed at the same time the undecidability of various subclasses of the full predicate logic. It has been shown in a number of works, which started appearing well before 1930, that the decision problem for the set of all formulae of the predicate logic is reducible to the decision problem for various subclasses of this set, each consisting of formulae in the prenex normal form with certain simple prefixes. The best known example

of such a subclass consists of formulae with the Skolem prefix
$\bigvee_{x_1} \dots \bigvee_{x_n} \bigwedge_{y_1} \dots \bigwedge_{y_m} M$, where M has no quantifiers. It may indeed
be shown quite easily that to each formula A of the predicate logic
there is a formula B of the form $\bigwedge_{x_1} \dots \bigwedge_{x_n} \bigvee_{y_1} \dots \bigvee_{y_m} M$ such that B
is satisfiable if and only if A is satisfiable (*cf.* Gödel [53]). Many
other classes of formulae with the same property have been found;
they are sometimes called "reduction types". An account of them
can be found in Surányi [219].

The reduction to the Skolem type of formulae as well as most of
the other reductions have been obtained by means of combinatorial
methods: one expresses the fact that a given formula A has a
model and tries to give to the resulting expression as simple a form
as possible.

A reduction of a different kind was found recently by Büchi [12]
and somewhat later by Moore, Wang and Kahr [86]. Instead of
expressing in a simple form the satisfiability of a formula A they
used a reduction to problems connected with Turing machines (or,
equivalently, with Markov's algorithms). Büchi showed that with
each Turing machine one can correlate a formula $F = \bigwedge_x A(x) \wedge$
$\bigwedge_x \bigvee_y \bigwedge_z B(x, y, z)$ such that F is satisfiable if and only if the corresponding machine ultimately stops. It follows that the class of
provable formulae $\bigvee_x P(x) \vee \bigvee_x \bigwedge_y \bigvee_z Q(x, y, z)$ (where P and Q do
not contain quantifiers) is not computable. Moore, Wang and Kahr
improved this result by showing that the class of true formulae
$\bigvee_x \bigwedge_y \bigvee_z Q(x, y, z)$ is not computable. It is worth while to mention
that the problem whether a formula of this form (or of Büchi's form
above) is satisfiable is algorithmically decidable (*cf.* lecture V).

The prefix problem which we have so far considered is interesting
in itself but seems rather artificial. Deeper problems arise when we
consider axiomatic theories and ask the question whether the sets
of their theorems are computable or not.

The first result of this kind is due to Church who proved (in effect)
that the set of theorems provable in Peano's arithmetic is not computable. Let us sketch a modern proof of this result.

Let T be a theory satisfying the following conditions:

1°. There is an infinite sequence of symbols $\varDelta_0, \varDelta_1, \dots$ such
that each formula of the form $\neg (\varDelta_i = \varDelta_j)$ is provable in T for $i \neq j$.

2°. Each primitive recursive relation is strongly representable in T.

3°. There is a formula $M(x, y)$ which strongly represents the relation $\leq$ in T and has the property that the formulae $M(x, y) \lor M(y, x)$ and $M(x, \mathit{\Delta}_n) \equiv [(x = \mathit{\Delta}_0) \lor \ldots \lor (x = \mathit{\Delta}_n)]$ are provable in T for each n.

Under these assumptions the set of provable formulae of T is not computable.

Indeed, let A and B be two recursively enumerable sets of integers which cannot be separated by computable sets (see p. 66). Since they are recursively enumerable, they can be defined in the form $A = \left\{n : \bigvee_{p} R(n, p)\right\}$, $B = \left\{m : \bigvee_{q} S(m, q)\right\}$ where R and S are primitive recursive relations. Let F and G be formulae which strongly represent R and S in T. Then the formulae

$$F' : \bigvee_{y} \left\{F(x, y) \land \bigwedge_{z} [M(z, y) \rightarrow \neg\, G(x, z)]\right\},$$

$$G' : \bigvee_{y} \left\{[G(x, y) \land \bigwedge_{z} [M(z, y) \rightarrow \neg\, F(x, z)]\right\}$$

weakly represent A and B and satisfy the condition that the formula $\neg\, [F'(x) \lor G'(x)]$ is provable in T.

Let us now assume that the set of provable formulae of T is computable and let $C = \left\{n : F'(\mathit{\Delta}_n) \text{ is provable in } T\right\}$. Hence C is computable, $A \subset C$ and $C \cap B = 0$, which contradicts the assumption of the inseparability of A and B.

The idea of this proof is due to Rosser [187].

As we see we proved not only the undecidability of T but also the undecidability of an arbitrary consistent extension of T. Theories each consistent extension of which is undecidable are called essentially undecidable.[1] Many examples of such theories are known. An example of a finitely axiomatizable and essentially undecidable theory was given on p. 22. Other examples can be found in [231].

Putnam [162] has shown the essential undecidability of an arbitrary theory T based on a recursively enumerable set of axioms in which every computable set is strongly representable. In order to obtain this result he uses the Gödel substitution function and constructs a formula F such that F is provable in T if and only if its Gödel number n belongs to a preassigned set strongly representable in T. It follows at once that this set cannot coincide with the set of Gödel numbers of the theorems of T; thus the latter set is not computable.

---

[1] The notion of essential undecidability coincides with that of essential incompleteness introduced on p. 22.

For further discussion of the question which theories are essentially undecidable, see Shoenfield [206]. It is proved in his paper that weak representability of all computable sets in T does not entail the essential undecidability of T.

Theories which are essentially undecidable and finitely axiomatizable can be used to establish undecidability of various theories. This method was devised by Tarski [231] who formulated the following test: If τ is an essentially undecidable and finitely axiomatizable theory, if T is a consistent theory and if T and τ have a common consistent extension, then T is undecidable. Using this test Tarski proved, among other things, the undecidability of the theory of groups and of the theory of lattices. It is remarkable that surprisingly weak theories prove to be undecidable; for instance, the theory whose primitive terms are two binary relations and whose axioms state that these relations are reflexive, symmetric, and transitive is undecidable. (If only one equivalence relation is considered, the theory is decidable.) This theory was discussed by Janiczak [84] and H. Rogers [184].

Another highly interesting method was found not long ago by Rabin [170] who showed that one can in many cases dispense with the use of essentially undecidable theories in proofs of undecidability.

Let T and T_1 be two theories whose primitive terms are R and R_1; we assume that R and R_1 denote binary relations. Let T_1 be undecidable. We require that T_1 be interpretable in T in the following sense: There are formulae $D(R, x)$ and $A(R, x, y)$ of T such that (i) all axioms of T_1 go over into theorems of T if the universe of T_1 is interpreted as the set of elements satisfying $D(R, x)$ and R_1 as the relation defined by $A(R, x, y)$; (ii) every model M_1 of T_1 can be obtained from a suitable model M of T by taking as the universe of M_1 the set $\{a : \models_M D[R_M, a]\}$ and as the interpretation of R_1 the relation $\{<a, b> : \models_M A[R_M, a, b]\}$. If these assumptions are satisfied, then T is undecidable.

In order to see this, let us denote, for any formula $F_1(R_1)$ of T_1, by $F(R)$ the formula of T obtained from F_1 by the process described in (i). Since it can be decided, for each formula of T, whether it does or does not correspond to a formula of T_1, it suffices to show that F is provable in T if and only if F_1 is provable in T_1. In one direction this follows from (i). Now assume that F_1 is not provable in T_1; by completeness theorem there is then a model M_1 of T_1 in which F_1 is false. Using (ii), we infer that there is a model M of T

in which F is false; whence Rabin's result follows. Obviously the assumption that R and R_1 are binary is not essential in this proof.

The following example (due to Rabin) will illustrate his method.

Let $\boldsymbol{T_1}$ be the theory whose unique primitive term is a k-ary relation R_1 and $\boldsymbol{T}$ the theory whose only primitive term is a binary relation R. No extra-logical axioms are assumed in either theory. Take as D the formula $\neg \bigvee_{y} (xRy)$ and as $A(R, x_1, \ldots, x_k)$ the formula $\bigvee_{u} [(uR^k u) \wedge (uR^1 x_1) \wedge (uR^2 x_2) \wedge \ldots \wedge (uR^k x_k)]$, where $uR^1 x$ means the same as uRx and where $uR^n x$ is defined (by induction) as $\bigvee_{v} [(uRv) \wedge (vR^{n-1}x)]$. E.g. if $k = 3$, the formula $A(R, x_1, x_2, x_3)$ is true just in case when the diagram of R looks as follows:

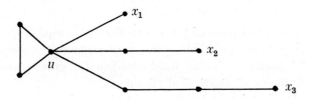

In this diagram points other than x_1, x_2, x_2 denote elements not satisfying the formula D.

This simple method of Rabin's is in many cases surprisingly efficient.

Slightly different from the problem of decidability of theories is the problem of decidability of models. For every $\boldsymbol{M}$ we may consider the set $T(\boldsymbol{M})$ of those formulae which are true in $\boldsymbol{M}$ and ask whether this set is computable. This problem is obviously equivalent with the decision problem for a theory $\boldsymbol{T}$ whose axioms are all the formulae of $T(\boldsymbol{M})$; thus we do not know a priori whether the axioms of $\boldsymbol{T}$ form a recursive set. For this reason not all methods mentioned in connection with the decision problem for theories can be applied to the decision problem of models.

In most cases we may establish the undecidability of a model $\boldsymbol{M}$ by showing that integers and the usual arithmetical operations on them are definable in $\boldsymbol{M}$; cf. Robinson [179] and J. Robinson [176]. These investigations often use rather deep results of purely mathematical character.

An interesting open problem is the decision problem for the model consisting of all the subsets of the real line and of the Boolean relations together with the additional relation: X is the closure of Y. This problem was formulated by Grzegorczyk [65] who established the undecidability of various models of similar character but was not able to solve the seemingly simplest case of a one dimensional space.

Many other decision problems are known in mathematics and especially in algebra. Let us mention the problem known as the word problem for semigroups: we consider a finite alphabet $\{a, b, \ldots, k\}$ and "words" in this alphabet, *i.e.* arbitrary finite (possibly void) sequences of these letters. Let $(S_1', S_1''), \ldots, (S_n', S_n'')$ be a finite list consisting of pairs of words. We call two words (S', S'') equivalent if S'' can be obtained from S' by a finite number of transformations each of which consists of a replacement in a given word w of a segment identical with S_i' by the word S_i'' or conversely $(i = 1, 2, \ldots, n)$. Let E be the set of pairs (S', S'') such that S' is equivalent to S''. Is E a computable set? This is the word problem for semigroups. We can formulate a similar word problem for groups and other decision problems of algebraical character.

Markov [138] and Post [161] reduced the word problem for semigroups to the problem whether any given Turing machine will eventually stop. This yields a negative solution to the word problem. The word problem for groups, which is much more difficult, was solved by Novikov [158]; simpler solutions were found by Boone [9] and other algebraists. We mention these results only briefly since in spite of their importance for algebra they have been used neither in logic nor in the study of foundations of mathematics. It should be stressed, however, that the theory of computable functions created by logicians in order to discuss philosophical and metamathematical problems proved decisive during the early phases of the study of algebraical decision problems. It can safely be said that these algebraical problems would have remained unsettled had not logicians developed the theory of decision problems for uninterpreted and syntactically described logical calculi.

Lecture XIII

The theory of models

The modern form of semantics is the theory of models. Some of its results are quite old. For instance, the Skolem—Löwenheim theorem dating back to 1917 is of basic importance for this theory. The systematic development of model theory was initiated by Tarski in the early fifties [227]. His ideas proved so fruitful that model theory is at present one of the most important parts of the foundational study. The theory has also close ties with abstract algebra, and it has found numerous applications.

The abstract scheme of model theory is as follows: We are given a language L and a class C of objects called models (or realizations) of sentences of L. There is also given a relation between sentences and models which we shall call the satisfaction relation and express by words as follows: "Model M satisfies the sentence F" (or "The sentence F is true in M"). We do not assume that sentences are necessarily finite sequences of letters; they may be abstract objects of quite arbitrary character. The language is determined not by the nature of these objects but by the operations performable on them. Thus in various applications we consider languages in which the class of sentences is not denumerable or in which we are allowed to form infinite conjunctions or disjunctions or in which each sentence is an infinite (perhaps even transfinite) sequence of symbols. Also the nature of models is quite arbitrary. In most cases they consist of a set (which we call the universe of the model) and a sequence of relations which correspond to the predicates of the language. This case is by far not the only possible one, however. The great flexibility of model theory is largely due to this freedom in the choice of the language and of the class of models.

We shall write $M \in E(F)$ or $\models_M F$ if the sentence F is true in the model M. For a set X of sentences we write $M \in E(X)$ if each formula F in X is true in M. M is then called a model of X. If X is the set of axioms of a theory, then we also say that M is a model of this theory. We say that a sentence F is a consequence of X if $E(X) \subset E(F)$; the set of all the consequences of X is denoted by $Cn(X)$. The operation Cn has the well known properties of a closure operation: $X \subset Cn(X)$ and $Cn(Cn(X)) = Cn(X)$.

The theory of models is best known in the case in which L is the first-order predicate logic with identity. Sentences of L are then first-order formulae without free variables. This case will be treated in the present lecture. We shall impose no limitations on the number of predicates in L, however, and we shall assume that there are arbitrarily many individual constants in L.

A model is defined as a sequence consisting of a set A (the universe of the model) and of a family of relations in A and of elements of A. This family is indexed by the predicates and the individual constants of L. In this way a relation between the elements of A is correlated with each predicate P of L and an element of A is correlated with each constant of L. We assume that the number of arguments of the relation correlated with P is the same as the number of arguments of P. The satisfaction relation is defined in the usual way explained in lecture III.

In order to simplify our terminology we shall sometimes identify a model with its universe. In this sense we speak of the cardinal number of a model or of an object being an element of the model.

Three relations between models are of importance for us:

1. We say that a model M_1 is a submodel of M_2 or that M_2 is an extension of M_1 (in symbols $M_1 \subset M_2$) if (i) the universe A_1 of M_1 is a subset of the universe A_2 of M_2; (ii) the relations of M_1 are obtained from those of M_2 by restricting them to A_1; (iii) the interpretations of individual constants are the same in both models.

2. A model M_1 is an elementary submodel of M_2 (or M_2 is an elementary extension of M_1, in symbols $M_1 < M_2$) if $M_1 \subset M_2$ and the following condition is satisfied: whenever F is a formula and $a, b, \ldots$ are elements of M_1 then the conditions $\models_{M_1} F[a, b, \ldots]$ and $\models_{M_2} F[a, b, \ldots]$ are equivalent.

3. Two models M_1 and M_2 are elementarily equivalent (in symbols $M_1 \equiv M_2$) if $M_1 \in E(F) \equiv M_2 \in E(F)$ for each sentence F.

Note that these three relations are meaningful not only in the case when L is the first-order logic but in all cases when we have defined the relation of satisfaction. In order for definitions 1 and 3 to be meaningful it is not even necessary to have defined the relation of satisfaction for formulae with free variables.

The relation $M_1 < M_2$ evidently implies $M_1 \subset M_2$ but not conversely. A connection between the notions of elementary extension and elementary equivalence has been established by Keisler [90]; see p. 130.

Relations 1 and 3 were introduced by Tarski [227], relation 2 by Tarski and Vaught [232].

We shall now discuss the Skolem—Löwenheim theorem.

Analyzing the original proof due to Skolem one obtains the following result (Tarski—Vaught [232]): If m is an infinite cardinal not less than the cardinal m_0 of the constants and predicates of L, and if M is a model of a power $k > m$, then for every cardinal p such that $k \geq p \geq m$ there is a model M_1 of power p such that $M_1 < M$. This theorem is called the downward Skolem—Löwenheim theorem.

A completely different theorem called in the recent literature the upward Skolem—Löwenheim theorem was proved for the first time by Tarski in a note to [209] (*cf.* Tarski—Vaught [232]): If m is a cardinal satisfying the conditions of the previous theorem and M is a model of power m, then for every cardinal $q \geq m$ there is a model M_2 of cardinality q such that $M_2 > M$.

The upward Skolem—Löwenheim theorem results easily from the compactness theorem:

If $E(X_1) \neq 0$ for every finite subset of a set X, then $E(X) \neq 0$.

For a language L with at most denumerably many constants and predicates this theorem was first proved by Gödel [53] (*cf.* lecture V). The general result is due to Malcev [134] who also first applied this theorem to algebra. A modern proof of the compactness theorem will be sketched in lecture XVI.

The different Skolem—Löwenheim theorems belong to the most important results in the theory of models. We shall show how they can be applied in order to characterize what are known as the spectra of sets of sentences.

Let X be a set of sentences of L. We shall call the spectrum of X the class of cardinals m such that $E(X)$ contains models of power m. It follows from the Skolem—Löwenheim theorems that if the spectrum of X contains at least one cardinal $\geq m_0$, then it contains all cardinals $\geq m_0$.

The part of the spectrum consisting of cardinals $< m_0$ is not very well understood even in the simplest case when $m_0 = \aleph_0$. Let us call a set K of integers the finite part of the spectrum of X (or of a single sentence F) if K is the intersection of the spectrum of X (or of F) and of the set of all integers. Scholz [194] asked whether all computable sets are finite parts of the spectra of single formulae. This question has been answered in the negative by Asser [4]. The finite parts of spectra thus form a subclass of the class of ccmputable sets, but the structure of this class is still unknown. For instance, one does not know whether the intersection of two sets in this class is also a member of the class. Some partial results on the finite parts of spectra were given in [151].

Rabin [166] has shown that the upward Skolem—Löwenheim theorem is in general not true if one drops the assumption that the power of M is not less than m_0. He gave a counter-example with $m_0 = 2^{\aleph_0}$. Rabin's paper illustrates the difficulties which we may expect in studying the initial parts of spectra.

Another simple but very fruitful application of Skolem—Löwenheim theorems is provided by new methods of completeness proofs. Since a complete theory with a recursively enumerable set of axioms is decidable, these methods often enable us to establish the decidability of a theory without the cumbersome calculations which are unavoidable in the elimination method discussed in lecture XII.

The first method to be discussed is based on the following lemma which immediately results from the definitions of the notions involved: A theory T is complete if and only if any two of its models are elementarily equivalent.

Let now T be a theory with at most denumerably many constants and predicates ($m_0 = \aleph_0$) and assume that there are no finite models M of T. We shall say that T is categorical in power m (Łoś [126], Vaught [236]) if any two models of T with the cardinal number m are isomorphic. Using the Skolem—Löwenheim theorems and the lemma given above we obtain the theorem: If a theory T satisfying the assumptions given above is categorical in an infinite power m, then it is complete (Vaught [236]). The following examples show the efficacy of this theorem:

(1) According to a classical theorem due to Cantor any two linearly ordered sets which are denumerable, dense and have no first or last element are isomorphic. Let T_1 be a theory with one binary predicate P based on axioms which state that the universe is densely ordered by P and has no first or last element. By Vaught's theorem T_1 is complete and hence decidable. We call T_1 the theory of dense ordering. Its decidability can be proved by the elimination method but this proof, while not very difficult, is incomparably more involved than the above semantical proof.

(2) In a similar way we show that the theory T_2 of atomless Boolean algebras is complete.

(3) Let T_3 be a theory with two ternary predicates S, P and axioms stating that for every two elements x, y of the universe there is exactly one $s = x + y$ such that $S(x, y, s)$ and exactly one $p = xy$ such that $P(x, y, p)$ and further that the universe is an algebraically closed field with characteristic zero.

Since one proves in algebra that any two algebraically closed fields with the same characteristic and the same power $m > \aleph_0$ are isomorphic, we obtain the result that the theory T_3 is complete and hence decidable.

The same result is also true for the theory $T_3(p)$ which we obtain from T_3 by dropping the axioms concerning the characteristic 0 and assuming instead of them an axiom stating that the characteristic of the field is p.

In order to avoid possible misunderstandings we add a few more comments on the axioms of T_3 and $T_3(p)$. Both these theories are based on an infinite number of axioms. Indeed, in order to express in the language L that a field is algebraically closed we must admit axioms which state that all quadratic equations, all equations of degree 3, all equations of degree 4 *etc.* have roots. For each degree we have thus a separate axiom. The fact that the field has characteristic 0 is expressed by the axioms

$$(x + x = 0) \rightarrow (x = 0), (x + x + x) \rightarrow (x = 0), (x + x + x + x = 0) \rightarrow$$
$$(x = 0), \dots.$$

which again form an infinite sequence.

In the usual expositions of the field theory all these axioms would be replaced by a finite number of sentences. These sentences would however involve the notions of polynomial and integer and hence would not belong to the first-order language on which theories T_3 and $T_3(p)$ are based. A theory based on this less elementary language, while mathematically more convenient, is much less interesting for a logician. No completeness result holds for this less elementary theory.

(4) Kochen [110] has obtained by the method described above Tarski's result that the theory of addition and multiplication of real numbers is decidable.

In view of these applications it would be desirable to have criteria of the categoricity of theories in a given infinite power. No such criteria are known in the general case. For $m = \aleph_0$ the following beautiful result was found by Ryll—Nardzewski [188] and (somewhat later but independently) by Svenonius [219a] and Engeler [32]: If a theory T with at most denumerably many predicates and constants is complete, then it is categorical in power $\aleph_0$ if and only if for each integer n the Boolean algebra of its formulae with at most n free variables is finite.

Partial results for the case $m > \aleph_0$ can be found in Vaught [237] and [239a]; the latter paper contains a survey of all results obtained so far in the study of this problem as well as a complete bibliography.

Łoś asked in [126] whether a theory categorical in a power $m > \aleph_0$ is categorical in every non-denumerable power. This very difficult problem was solved (positively) by Morley [147].

The work on the notion of categoricity in a given power is still in progress.

We shall now discuss another semantical method of establishing completeness of theories.

Let M be a model with the universe A; for simplicity we assume that there is just one relation R in M and that it is a binary one. We adjoin to the language L constants for all the elements of A, and denote by t_a the constant denoting a. The set consisting of all formulae $P(t_a, t_b)$ where a and b are elements of A such that aRb, of all formulae $t_a \neq t_b$ such that a and b are different elements of A and of all formulae $\neg P(t_a, t_b)$ where a and b are elements of A such that it is not the case that $a R b$ is called the diagram of M and is denoted by $D(M)$.

Let now T be a theory and X its set of axioms. We call T a model-complete theory if for every model $M \in E(X)$ the set $X \cup D(M)$ is complete. This notion was introduced by A. Robinson [180]. Before we show how to use it in proofs of completeness we give a few examples which show that the notions of completeness and of model-completeness are different from each other:

The theory T_1 is complete and model-complete.

The theory of linear order of type $\omega^* + \omega$ (cf. page 110) is complete but not model-complete. Indeed, if M_0 is a model of this theory consisting of integers (positive and negative) ordered by the relation $\leq$, then the sentence $\neg \bigvee_x [P(t_0, x) \wedge P(x, t_1) \wedge (x \neq t_0) \wedge (x \neq t_1)]$ is neither provable nor disprovable in $X \cup D(M_0)$.

The theory of algebraically closed fields obtained from the theory T_3 by dropping all the axioms referring to the characteristic of the field is incomplete but model-complete. Indeed, the sentence $\bigwedge_{x,y} [S(x,x,y) \to S(y,y,y)]$ which states that the characteristic of the field is 2 is independent of the axioms. On the other hand if M is a model of the theory then the set $X \cup D(M)$ is complete. If the characteristic of M is 0, then the set $X \cup D(M)$ is equivalent to the axioms of T_3; if the characteristic of M is p, then this set is equivalent to the set of axioms of $T_3(p)$; hence the set is always complete.

Robinson [180] has established a necessary and sufficient condition for model-completeness of a theory which can be tested rather easily. The condition says that for every model M of T, for every extension M' of M which is also a model of T, and for every sentence B of the form $\bigvee_{x_1, \ldots, x_k} Y$ where Y is a conjunction of atomic formulae or of their negations, the conditions $M \in E(B)$ and $M' \in E(B)$ are equivalent. Using the expression of Robinson: existential sentences B are persistent, *i.e.* their validity in M is preserved by extensions of M to any larger model M' (under the assumption that the axioms X of T are true both in M and in M').

Let us sketch briefly a proof of Robinson's result.

We first assume that T is a model-complete theory. If an existential formula B is true in M, then it is obviously true in an extension M' of M. If B is false in M, then by the completeness of $X \cup D(M)$, the sentence $\neg B$ is a consequence of $X \cup D(M)$, since the consequences of $X \cup D(M)$ are true in M. Since the diagram of M is contained in the diagram of M', we obtain that $\neg B$ is a consequence of $X \cup D(M')$ and hence that $\neg B$ is true in M', *i.e.* B is false in M.

Now we assume that T is not model-complete. Let M be a model such that $M \in E(X)$ and Z a sentence independent of $X \cup D(M)$. We can assume that Z is in the prenex normal form beginning with an existential quantifier and that no sentence in such form with fewer quantifiers is independent of $X \cup D(M')$ for any model M' of T. Put $Z = \bigvee_x Q(x)$.

Since $X \cup D(M) \cup \{Z\}$ is consistent there is an extension M' of M such that $M' \in E(X \cup \{Z\})$. Hence M' contains an element a such that $Q(t_a)$ is true in M'. Since $Q(t_a)$ has less quantifiers than Z we obtain $Q(t_a) \in Cn(X \cup D(M'))$ whence it results easily that $Q(t_a) \in Cn(X \cup \{Y(t_{a_1}, \ldots, t_{a_n})\})$ where Y is a conjunction of finitely many sentences in $D(M')$.

It follows easily that $\left[\bigvee\limits_{x_1,\ldots,x_n} Y(x_1, \ldots, x_n) \to Z\right] \in Cn(X)$ and

hence the sentence $B = \bigvee\limits_{x_1,\ldots,x_n} Y(x_1, \ldots, x_n)$ is not provable

from $X \cup D(M)$. It follows that B is false in $D(M)$. On the other hand B is true in M'. Thus the incompleteness of $X \cup D(M)$ contradicts the Robinson's condition.

We shall now show how Robinson uses his theorem in the study of completeness. Let us call M a prime model for a theory T if every model M' in which the axioms of T are true contains a sub-model of T isomorphic with M. Robinson's main theorem states:

If a model-complete theory T admits a prime model M, then it is complete.

Indeed, we shall show that theorems of T coincide with sentences true in M. It is sufficient to show that if a sentence Z is true in M, it is provable. Otherwise there would exist an extension M' of M such that $M' \in E(X)$ and Z would be false in M'. Hence, by the model-completeness $\neg Z$ would be a consequence of $X \cup D(M')$. But this is clearly impossible since Z is a consequence of $X \cup D(M)$ and $D(M)$ is a subset of $D(M')$.

Because of its assumptions Robinson's theorem is applicable only to a limited class of theories. One of the most important applications was Robinson's result [181] showing the decidability of the set of those first-order sentences involving the predicates $x = y$, $x \leqq y$, $x = y + z$, $x = y.z$ and "x is an algebraic number" which are true for the real numbers. This extension of Tarski's decidability result, which we discussed in lecture XII, could hardly be obtained by the method of elimination of quantifiers.

Further indications concerning completeness proofs using model-theoretical notions can be found in Robinson's book [183].

Another important part of model theory depends on a theorem known as Craig's interpolation lemma [25]. This result is a purely syntactic theorem dealing with the provability of formulae in the first-order logic without identity. It says that if $F(P, Q_1, \ldots, Q_k, x_1, \ldots, x_m)$ and $G(P', Q_1, \ldots, Q_k, x_1, \ldots, x_m)$ are two formulae with the free (predicate and individual) variables indicated and if the implication $F \to G$ is provable in logic then there is a formula $H = H(Q_1, \ldots, Q_k, x_1, \ldots, x_m)$ such that both implications $F \to H$ and $H \to G$ are provable in logic. The essential point is of course that the interpolation formula H contains freely only those variables which are free in F and in G.

We shall reformulate Craig's lemma using semantic notions. In order to simplify the notations we shall assume that $m = 0$ and $k = 1$ and write Q instead of Q_1. Furthermore we assume that P and Q are both binary predicates.

Let A be a fixed infinite set and let M be the family of all models of the form $<A, R>$ where $R \subset A \times A$. If H is a formula with the free variable Q, then we denote by U_H the set of all models $\boldsymbol{M}$ in M such that $|=_{\boldsymbol{M}} H[R]$, i.e. H is satisfied in $\boldsymbol{M}$ under the interpretation of Q as R. If F has the free variables P, Q, then we denote by V_F the set of models $\boldsymbol{M}$ in M for which there exists a relation $S \subset A \times A$ such that F is satisfied in the model $\boldsymbol{M}^* = <A, S, R>$ obtained from $\boldsymbol{M}$ by adjunction of the new relation S.

Craigs lemma is equivalent to the following separation principle: If $F = F(P, Q)$ and $G = G(P, Q)$ are formulae such that $V_F \cap V_G = 0$, then there are formulae $H = H(Q)$, $K = K(Q)$ such that $V_F \subset U_H$, $V_G \subset U_K$ and $U_H \cap U_K = 0$.

This formulation of Craig's theorem was a starting point of an extensive work undertaken by Addison in which he tried to establish a common basis for set-theoretical and logical separation principles. (See [3 a].)

The equivalence of this statement with Craig's lemma is a simple corollary to the completeness theorem.

Proofs of Craig's lemma were given, besides by Craig himself, by Lyndon and other authors; see literature quoted in [131].

In order to illustrate the uses of Craig's lemma we shall give a proof of a theorem due to Beth concerning the theory of definitions [6]. This theorem was proved by Beth before Craig in a more complicated way.

We mentioned already in lecture III a method (due in principle to Padoa and stated precisely by Tarski) of proving independence of a primitive notion P of a theory $\boldsymbol{T}$ from other primitive notions $Q_1, \ldots, Q_k$ of $\boldsymbol{T}$. The Padoa—Tarski theorem states that if there are two models $\boldsymbol{M} = <A, R, S_1, \ldots, S_k>$, $\boldsymbol{M}' = <A, R', S_1, \ldots, S_k>$ of $\boldsymbol{T}$ such that $R \neq R'$ then P is independent of $Q_1, \ldots, Q_k$ in $\boldsymbol{T}$.

Beth's theorem says now that this method is always applicable: If there are no models $\boldsymbol{M}$, $\boldsymbol{M}'$ with the properties mentioned above, then P can be defined in $\boldsymbol{T}$ with the help of $Q_1, \ldots, Q_k$ alone.

Proof: Using the completeness theorem we obtain, that if there are no models M, M' required in Padoa's method then there is a finite conjunction K of axioms of T such that the formula

$$K(R, Q_1, \ldots, Q_k) \rightarrow \big\{K(R', Q_1, \ldots, Q_k) \rightarrow [R(x_1, \ldots, x_p) \rightarrow$$
$$R'(x_1, \ldots, x_p)]\big\}$$

is provable in logic. If $L(Q_1, \ldots, Q_k, x_1, \ldots, x_p)$ is an interpolating formula for the formulae

$$F : K(R, Q_1, \ldots, Q_k) \wedge R(x_1, \ldots, x_p),$$

$$G : K(R', Q_1, \ldots, Q_k) \rightarrow R'(x_1, \ldots, x_p),$$

then $R(x_1, \ldots, x_p) \equiv L(Q_1, \ldots, Q_k, x_1, \ldots, x_p)$ is provable in T and hence R is definable in T by means of $Q_1, \ldots, Q_k$ alone.

Important extensions of Craig's lemma are due to Lyndon. We shall discuss only one of his results; a full account is given in [131].

First we define by induction the phrase: "An atomic formula $M(t_1, \ldots, t_k)$ (where $t_1, \ldots, t_k$ are terms) occurs positively (negatively) in a formula F". If F and M coincide, then M occurs positively in F. If M occurs positively (negatively) in F, then it occurs positively (negatively) in $F \vee G$, $G \vee F$, $F \wedge G$, $G \vee F$, $G \rightarrow F$, $\bigvee_x F$, $\bigwedge_x F$ and negatively (positively) in $\neg F$ and in $F \rightarrow G$.

If all the atomic formulae involving R occur positively in F, then we say that R occurs positively in F.

Lyndon's generalization of Craig's lemma is now this: Let F and G be formulae as in Craig's lemma and assume that Q_j occurs positively (negatively) in F and in G; then there exists an interpolation formula H in which Q_j also occurs positively (negatively). It follows from Lyndon's theorem that if a formula F containing a predicate Q has the property that its validity is preserved under extensions of Q, then F is equivalent to a formula in which Q occurs positively. More precisely, the assumption means that the condition $M \in E(F)$ implies $M' \in E(F)$ for each M' obtained from M by replacing the relation S which interprets in M the predicate Q by a relation $S' \supset S$.

This result solved a problem proposed by Marczewski in [137]. It is one of the many results in model theory which relate the set-theoretical properties of models with the syntactic properties of sentences true in these models. We shall consider below some other results of this sort.

Let us consider a class F of models and assume that F contains with each M every model isomorphic to M (we disregard at present the set-theoretical difficulties involved in this definition). We call F an elementary class if there is a set X of first-order sentences such that $F = E(X)$. This terminology is due to Tarski [227]. Our program is to characterize the elementary classes among all possible classes F and also to study relations between the form of sentences which belong to X and the set-theoretical properties of F.

Lyndon's theorem fits in this program since it can be rephrased as follows: If an elementary class F has the property that it contains with each M any model M' obtained by replacing S by a relation $S' \supset S$, then $F = E(X)$ where each formula A in X contains the predicate Q positively.

Historically the first (and simplest) result of this kind was obtained by Tarski [228] and, independently, by Łoś [127]. It says that if a class F contains with each M all the submodels of M and if F is an elementary class, then there is a set X of sentences such that $F = E(X)$ and that all the elements of X are general sentences (*i.e.* have the form $\bigwedge_{xy\ldots} H$ where H does not contain quantifiers).

Another result of this kind due to Łoś—Suszko [130], and also obtained by Chang [14], characterizes elementary classes closed with respect to the operation of forming the union of an increasing sequence of models.

All these results have been essentially generalized by Keisler [88].

Many authors have given various set-theoretical characterizations of elementary classes. Thus *e.g.* Tajmanov [221] obtained a simple characterization in topological terms. He introduced a topology in the class of all models by taking as neighbourhoods of a model M the classes $E(A)$ where A is any formula true in M. Elementary classes are just closed subsets of this space. Many other characterizations have been shown by Tajmanov to follow from this simple result.

The deepest result in this direction is due to Keisler [89] who proved (using the generalized continuum hypothesis) that a class F is elementary if and only if it is closed with respect to the operation of forming reduced Cartesian powers and its complement $-F$ is closed with respect to the operation of forming reduced Cartesian products (these notions will be explained in lecture XVI). Less deep but independent of the continuum hypothesis are characterizations given by Kochen [110] who used other operations than those of forming reduced products and powers.

9

It is remarkable that in spite of their very abstract form these characterizations can be effectively used. For instance, Rabin [169] proved, using these criteria, that the class of groups G which are (isomorphic to) groups of automorphism of models M in $E(X)$ is always an elementary class and thus has the form $E(Y)$. Rabin's theorem states the existence of a set Y for any given X but his proof does not provide any means of actually constructing such a set, and is thus of great interest for evaluating non-effective methods in logic and set theory.

Another problem which has been studied extensively is that of giving set-theoretical criteria for the elementary equivalence of two models.

Keisler [90] proved that $M_1 \equiv M_2$ if and only if some reduced powers of M_1 and M_2 are isomorphic to each other. It follows that $M_1 \equiv M_2$ if and only if there are two isomorphic models M_1' and M_2' such that $M_1 < M_1'$ and $M_2 < M_2'$. Kochen [110] gave a similar characterization of $\equiv$ in terms of other operations. Less sophisticated but very useful was a characterization given by Ehrenfeucht and Fraïssé.

Fraïssé's [41] definition uses a sequence of equivalence relations $\sim_n$. Let X_1, X_2 be finite subsets of the universes of M_1 and M_2. We write $X_1 \sim_0 X_2$ if the relations of both models restricted to X_1 and X_2 are isomorphic. Now assume that an equivalence relation $\sim_n$ between finite subsets of M_1, M_2 has already been defined. We define the relation $\sim_{n+1}$ as follows: $X_1 \sim_{n+1} X_2$ if for every x_1 in the universe of M_1 there is an x_2 in the universe of M_2 such that $X_1 \cup \{x_1\} \sim_n X_2 \cup \{x_2\}$ and conversely.

Fraïssé's theorem says that $M_1 \equiv M_2$ if and only if $0 \sim_n 0$ for each n.

Let us consider as an example the set N of all integers ordered by the $\leq$ relation (its order type is $\omega^* + \omega$) and an extension N' of N ordered by an extension $\leq'$ of the $\leq$-relation in type $\omega^* + \omega + \omega^* + \omega$. We assume that N is an initial segment of N'. Let $M_1 = \langle N, \leq \rangle$, $M_2 = \langle N', \leq' \rangle$ and let $X_1 \subset N$, $X_2 \subset N'$ be two finite sets with the same number of elements. We can decompose X_2 into a disjoint union $X_2 = X_2' \cup X_2''$ where $X_2' = X_2 \cap N$, $X_2'' = X_2 - N$. Let X_2' and X_2'' have p' and p'' elements. It is then easy to prove that $X_1 \sim_n X_2$ if and only if there are at least n

elements between the first p' and the last p'' elements of X_1. This implies, in particular, that $M_1 \equiv M_2$.

One could obtain the same result by using the elimination of quantifiers but the method based on Fraïssé's construction is much more conspicuous.

Ehrenfeucht obtained (independently) the same characterization as Fraïssé and expressed it in a very suggestive language of games [30]. He also showed how this characterization can be applied to solve various problems concerning definability of elements in models whose universes consist of ordinals.

We shall see, in the next lecture, that the Ehrenfeucht—Fraïssé method can be extended to certain languages different from the first-order language considered here.

The results of model theory presented here do not exhaust all which have been dealt with in the existing literature. The theory is still in the stage of very rapid development and will certainly find many new applications.

Lecture XIV

Theory of models for non-elementary languages

We mentioned already in lecture XIII that the scheme of the model theory is very general and applicable to various kinds of languages. Several attempts were made to apply this scheme to languages different from the language L of the first-order logic.

We shall report on results obtained for the following languages:

1. The language Q_a. This language differs from L by containing in addition to the symbols of L one new quantifier Q. The sentence $QxFx$ is true in a model $\boldsymbol{M}$ if and only if there are in $\boldsymbol{M}$ at least $\aleph_a$ elements which satisfy F in $\boldsymbol{M}$. We have thus one language with many different interpretations of the constant Q. The notion of a model is the same as in the case of the language L.

2. The language L_a^{II}. This language differs from L by containing variables $X, Y, \ldots$ for sets. A sentence $\bigvee_X F(X)$ is true in a model $\boldsymbol{M}$ if there is a subset of $\boldsymbol{M}$ whose power is $< \aleph_a$ which satisfies F in $\boldsymbol{M}$. Again we see that there is one syntactic structure of the language but a multitude of interpretations. The languages L_a^{II} are said to be of weak second-order. Again models are defined in the same way as in L.

3. The strong second-order language L^{II} has the same syntactic structure as L_a^{II} but a different interpretation of the set variables: the formula $\bigvee_X F(X)$ is true in a model $\boldsymbol{M}$ if there is a subset of $\boldsymbol{M}$ of any cardinality which satisfies $F(X)$ in $\boldsymbol{M}$.

4. The sequential second-order language L_0^s contains variables not for finite sets of elements but for finite sequences of them and also symbols for concatenation of two sequences and for forming a one-term sequence $<a>$ out of a given element a.

5. Higher order languages $L_a^{(n)}$ and $L^{(n)}$ are defined similarly as the languages L_a^{II} and L^{II}. It is possible to combine the methods of construction of these languages and require for instance that arbi-

trary subsets of a model be values of the first-order set-variables X, Y, ... but only finite sets be allowed as values for second-order set-variables *etc.*

6. The infinitistic language $L_{\omega_1, \, \omega_0}$. Let x_i, c_i for $i = 0, 1, 2, \ldots$ be individual variables and constants and let R_i be a predicate with p_i arguments $(i = 0, 1, 2, \ldots)$. Atomic formulae of $L_{\omega_1, \, \omega_0}$ are expressions $R_i(t_1, \ldots, t_{p_i})$ where each t_i is either a variable or a constant. The rules of formation of more complicated formulae are the same as in L with two additional infinitistic rules: if A_i is an infinite sequence of formulae, then $\sum_i A_i$ and $\prod_i A_i$ are formulae.

Models are just the ordinary models as in the case of L. A sentence $\sum_i A_i$ is true in M if and only if there is an i such that A_i is true in M; a sentence $\prod_i A_i$ is true in M if and only if each A_i is true in M.

Formulae of $L_{\omega_1, \, \omega_0}$ are infinitistic objects; thus even the syntax of this language can be studied only in strong systems of set theory.

In the symbol $L_{\omega_1, \, \omega_0}$ the first index ω_1 is the smallest cardinal larger than the cardinal number of terms in any disjunction or conjunction allowed in the language. The second index shows that only a finite number (*i.e.* a number $< \omega_0$) of variables can occur under a quantifier: we can form a sentence $\bigvee_{x_1, \ldots, x_n} F$ (which is, in fact, an abbreviation for $\bigvee_{x_1} \bigvee_{x_2} \ldots \bigvee_{x_n} F$) but we are not allowed to form a sentence $\bigvee_{\{x_1, x_2, \ldots\}} F$ with an infinite sequence of variables under the quantifier.

7. The infinitistic languages $L_{\omega_\mu, \, \omega_\nu}$ are defined similarly. For instance in $L_{\omega_2, \, \omega_1}$ we can form disjunctions and conjunctions of sequences of lengths $< \omega_2$ and also bind by a single quantifier strings of variables whose length is any ordinal $< \omega_1$.

These languages were introduced by Tarski and Scott [200]; the symbolism is due to C. Karp [87] who undertook an extensive study of these languages. The usual first-order logic is contained as a special case among the languages here considered: in fact $L = L_{\omega_0, \, \omega_0}$.

There exist various relations between the languages we enumerated. Thus *e.g.* Q_a is translatable into L_a^{II} and L_a^{II} into $L_{\omega_a, \, \omega_a}$.

The notions of submodel, elementary extension (with respect to a given language J), elementary equivalence (with respect to J), spectrum, elementary class (with respect to J) can easily be defined in a similar way as in the previous lecture. The same applies to the notion of (logical) consequence. However, not all results can be carried over to the more general theory which we consider here.

The main difference between the model theory for the language L and the model theories of the languages $1-7$ above is the failure of the compactness theorem in most of the latter. This theorem is false for the languages Q_0, L_a^{II}, L^{II}, L_0^s and most of the languages L_{ω_μ}, $_{\omega_\nu}$. For the languages Q_{a+1} Fuhrken [48] proved a remarkable theorem which implies that the compactness theorem is true in the model theory of these languages. It is not yet known whether this is also true for languages Q_a with a limit index.

The downward Skolem—Löwenheim theorem is valid (with some modifications concerning the minimal power of a model) for all languages defined above. This is no more true for the upward Skolem —Löwenheim theorem which fails for almost all of these languages (notice that we used the compactness theorem in the proof of the upward Skolem—Löwenheim theorem for the language L). Because of the failure of this theorem the structure of spectra in these languages is incomparably more involved than in the case of language L.

In this connection Hanf [73] proved a simple but interesting theorem valid for any language J in which the downward Skolem—Löwenheim theorem is true: for any such language there exists a cardinal $\mathfrak{f}$ (the "Hanf number of J") with the property that if a formula F has a model of power $\mathfrak{f}$, it also has a model of any power $> \mathfrak{f}$. Hanf's proof is not constructive and the actual determination of $\mathfrak{f}$ even for very simple languages presents great difficulties. From results of Morley [148] it follows $e.g.$ that for Q_0 the Hanf number is $\mathfrak{T}_{\omega_1}$ where the transfinite sequence $\mathfrak{T}_\xi$ is defined as follows: $\mathfrak{T}_0 = \aleph_0$, $\mathfrak{T}_{\xi+1} = 2^{\mathfrak{T}_\xi}$, $\mathfrak{T}_\lambda = \Sigma_{\xi < \lambda}\, \mathfrak{T}_\xi$ for limit numbers λ.

Montague [146] investigated spectra in higher-order languages $L^{(n)}$ and proved using essentially results of Hintikka [83] that with each formula of $L^{(n)}$ one can correlate a formula of $L^{(II)}$ with the same spectrum. This illustrates the difficulty of the spectrum problem for the language $L^{(II)}$.

The Fraïssé—Ehrenfeucht formulation of the equivalence of models can be carried over to several non-elementary languages. Let us sketch (after Fraïssé [42]) the relevant definitions for the language L_a^{II}.

Let M be a model with the universe A and A^n the set of all sequences $<x_1, \ldots, x_n>$ with $x_j \in A$ for $j = 1, 2, \ldots, n$. Let further $S_a(A)$ be the family of subsets of A of a power $< \aleph_a$ and $S_a(A)^n$ the set of all sequences $<X_1, \ldots, X_n>$ with $X_i \in S_a(A)$. We define a sequence of equivalence relations $\sim_k$ whose fields are triples $<M, x, X>$ where M is a model, $x \in A^n$, $X \in S_a(A)^n$ and n is an integer.

The relation $<M_1, x_1, X_1> \sim_0 <M_2, x_2, X_2>$ holds if and only if 1° the function correlating the consecutive terms $x_{11}, x_{12}, \ldots, x_{1n}$ of x_1 to the corresponding terms $x_{21}, x_{22}, \ldots, x_{2n}$ of x_2 is an isomorphism with respect to the relations of M_1 and M_2; 2° $x_{i1} \in X_{1j} \equiv x_{2i} \in X_{2j}$ for all $i, j \leq n$.

If $\sim_k$ is already defined, then we define $\sim_{k+1}$ as follows: the relation $<M_1, x_1, X_1> \sim_{k+1} <M_2, x_2, X_2>$ holds if and only if for arbitrary $z_1 \in A_1$ and $Z_1 \in S_a(A_1)$ there are $z_2 \in A_2$ and $Z_1 \in S_a(A_2)$ such that
$$<M_1, x_1{}^\frown<z_1>, X_1{}^\frown<Z_1>> \sim_k <M_2, x_2{}^\frown<z_2>, X_2{}^\frown<Z_2>>$$
and conversely.

With these definitions it is easy to show that two models M_1, M_2 are equivalent with respect to the language L_a^{II} if and only if $M_1 \sim_k M_2$ for each k.

For infinitistic languages $L_{\omega\mu}, \omega_0$ the sequence of relations $\sim_k$ can be extended into transfinite but even this transfinite sequence does not yield the full characterization of equivalence with respect to $L_{\omega\mu}, \omega_0$. These problems were investigated by Scott who found applications for them in the descriptive set theory [199]. See also [123 a].

Interesting and mostly not yet solved problems result when one investigates analogues of the completeness theorem for various generalizations of the language L. Let us call a sentence F of a language J true if it is true in all models. In case of the language L the set of true sentences is as we know recursively enumerable. For the language Q_0 one shows easily that this set is a Π_1^1-set which is not hyper-arithmetical and the same is true for the languages L_0^{II} and L_0^s. For Q_1 Vaught [239] established the unexpected fact (based on results of Fuhrken [48]) that the set of true sentences of this language is recursively enumerable. The problem has not yet been solved for all languages Q_a. For languages L_a^{II} ($a > 0$) and L^{II} only negative results are known; e.g. one knows that the set of true sentences of these languages are not analytic. The problem whether they are constructible in Gödel's sense is open. Still less is known in case of infinitistic languages $L_{\omega_\mu, \, \omega_\mu}$ because we are lacking suitable hierarchies which would allow us to express the analogues of the completeness theorem.

We shall devote the rest of this lecture to applications of model theories of generalized languages. Whereas there are as we saw in lecture XIII many applications of the usual model theory, the applications of the generalized one are rather scarce. Some of them are worth noticing, however.

1. Axiomatic theories based on the language L_0^s. Axiomatic theories usually considered in meta-mathematics are based on the first-order logic L and the notion of consequence used in them is the (syntactically defined) notion of consequence of L. It follows from the Skolem—Löwenheim theorem for L that such theories are never categorical unless the cardinalities of all their models do not surpass a fixed integer.

Tarski [229] was the first to realize that one often obtains interesting theories, if one bases them on other languages and appropriately changes the notion of consequence. Suppose for instance that we base a theory on the language L_0^s (the theory is then said to be of a weak second-order). We admit then as axioms certain sentences of L_0^s and call a sentence of L_0^s a theorem if it is a consequence of axioms *i.e.* if it is true in every model of the axioms. Such a theory is decidable only if all its models have just one element. Unless this assumption is satisfied, the set of theorems is not recursively enumerable. On the other hand many weak second order theories are categorical and hence complete. Moreover they are often more natural from the mathematical point of view, since we can define in them various notions not definable in the ordinary theories.

Let us take as an example the weak second-order theory of algebraically closed fields (Tarski [229]).

The notion of a polynomial is definable in such a theory (we can identify a polynomial with the sequence of its coefficients). We can also define the value of a polynomial for a given argument and thus express in a single sentence that a field is algebraically closed. Also the notion of characteristic is definable in the theory.

We saw in lecture XIII that the first-order theory of algebraically closed fields requires an infinite number of axioms; on the contrary the weak second-order theory is finitely axiomatizable.

Tarski (*l.c.*) was able to classify all equivalence types (with respect to L_0^s) of algebraically closed fields of a given characteristic. It turned out that fields with a given finite degree of transcendence form such a class; besides these classes there is still one equivalence class containing all algebraically closed fields with infinite degrees of transcendence. As an immediate corollary Tarski obtained the result that if a sentence of L_0^s is valid in the field of complex numbers it is valid in all algebraically closed fields with characteristic 0 and infinite degree of transcendence.

A similar "transfer principle" was obtained earlier by Tarski [226] for sentences of L as a simple corollary to the decidability of the elementary theory of addition and multiplication of complex numbers. Since the theory based on the language L_0^s is incomparably richer than the elementary theory, the new principle represents a much stronger result than the old one.

It follows from the result discussed above that the weak second-order theory of algebraically closed fields becomes complete, upon addition of axioms which determine the characteristic and the transcendence-degree of the field. Other examples of complete weak second-order theories are provided by the arithmetic of integers or of rationals. These theories are even categorical and, in addition, finitely axiomatizable of course with respect to the notion of consequence in L_0^s. The set of sentences of L_0^s which are valid in the field of real numbers is not finitely (and even not hyper-arithmetically axiomatizable (cf. [152]). It seems to us that the study of axiomatizability of weak second-order theories deserves a further study.

2. Applications of infinitistic logics $L_{\omega_\mu, \, \omega_\mu}$ to abstract set theory. We mentioned in lecture VI that the compactness theorem for the first-order logic follows from the existence of a maximal filter in an arbitrary Boolean algebra. A similar connection between the compactness theorem and the existence of certain filters subsists for infinitistic logics $L_{\omega_\mu, \, \omega_\mu}$.

In order to state this result we must first explain some set-theoretical notions. An ordinal μ is called regular if ω_μ cannot be represented as a limit of a transfinite sequence of a type $< \omega_\mu$ whose terms are $< \omega_\mu$. An ordinal μ is called inaccessible if it is regular and $m < \aleph_\mu \to 2^m < \aleph_\mu$.

Tarski [230] calls an ordinal μ strongly compact, if every set X of sentences of $L_{\omega_\mu, \, \omega_\mu}$ with cardinality $\aleph_\mu$ has the property: if every subset of X with a smaller cardinality is satisfiable, then so is X. The connection with the theory of filters established by Tarski is now this: a regular ordinal μ is strongly compact provided that the Boolean algebra B_μ of all subsets of a set of power $\aleph_\mu$ contains a maximal non-principal $\aleph_\mu$-multiplicative filter (*i.e.*, a filter F such that if $R \subset F$ and R has a power $< \aleph_\mu$, then the intersection of R belongs to F). This result reduces the question of existence of filters with the properties just mentioned to a meta-mathematical problem concerning the language $L_{\omega_\mu, \omega_\mu}$. Mathematicians interested in abstract set theory once tried for a long time to settle the question whether for the first inaccessible ordinal $\mu > 0$ the Boolean algebra B_μ contains a nonprincipal, $\aleph_\mu$-multiplicative maximal filter (for all smaller numbers the problem was solved long ago by Tarski and Ulam). The interest in this question is due to the fact that it is closely connected with the abstract measure theory.

Solving this problem proposed by Tarski Hanf [73] showed that the first inaccessible number $\mu > 0$ is strongly incompact whence in particular it follows that there is no filter of the kind indicated above. The measure-theoretic problem was thus solved by the use of the model theory of the language $L_{\omega_\mu, \omega_\mu}$. Hanf's construction showed, moreover, that many other regular ordinals are strongly incompact. The question whether one can assume without inconsistency that there are strongly compact ordinals is open and seems to be very difficult.

We shall outline Hanf's proof of incompactness of $L_{\omega_\mu, \omega_\mu}$ for the first inaccessible ordinal > 0. To obtain his result Hanf considered a set X of sentences of $L_{\omega_\mu, \omega_\mu}$ which describes an axiomatic theory of ordinals. All sentences of X contain but one predicate, *viz.* ϵ. We include in X the axiom of extensionality and the axiom of regularity in the form

$$\neg \bigvee_{v_0, v_1, \ldots} \prod_n (v_{n+1} \epsilon v_n).$$

Next we add to X sentences which state the existence of all ordinals $\xi < \omega_\mu$. Since each ordinal is equal to the set of its predecessors, it can be described by a formula $S_\xi(x)$ of $L_{\omega_\mu, \omega_\mu}$. *E.g.* for $\xi = \omega_1$, we have as the description of ξ the formula

$$\bigvee_v \left\{ \prod_{\xi < a} \bigwedge_u [(u \epsilon v_\xi \equiv \Sigma_{\tau < \xi} (u = v_\tau)] \wedge (v_{\omega_1} = x) \right\}$$

where v stands for the sequence $\{v_a\}$ of type $\omega_1 + 1$.

The sentences which we add to X have the form $\bigvee_x S_\xi(x)$.

Finally we add to X sentences which state (I) that all ordinals are smaller than the first inaccessible ordinal $> \omega$ and (II) that there exists a largest ordinal. While it is clear how to express (II), the sentence (I) is rather involved and cannot be given here. One obtains it expressing in our formal language the definition of various set-theoretical notions.

The cardinal number of X is $\aleph_\mu$. Each set $X_1 \subset X$ with a cardinality $< \aleph_\mu$ is satisfiable in a model of set-theoretical axioms containing only ordinals smaller than a fixed ordinal $< \omega_\mu$. The whole set X is not satisfiable since the largest ordinal Ω of the model (existing on account of (II)) would be smaller than μ (by (I)) but also would be $\geq \xi$ for every $\xi < \mu$ (since we have in X the axioms stating the existence of ξ and $\xi + 1$ for each individually given ξ). We thus obtain $\Omega \geq \mu$ and $\Omega < \mu$ which is a contradiction.

Tarski and Keisler [92] have shown that the results concerning filters in B_μ can be obtained directly without a detour via the meta-mathematics of the logic $L_{\omega_\mu, \, \omega_\mu}$. It remains a fact, however, that it was the model theory of infinitistic languages which has led Tarski and Hanf to discoveries in the abstract set theory.

Infinitistic languages are obviously not suitable as a basis for mathematics since even their syntax requires a strong set theory. The above examples show, however, that they are not just idle generalizations but valuable tools for obtaining new results.

Lecture XV

Problems in the foundations of set theory

The abstract set theory has contributed more than any other branch of mathematics to the development of foundational studies. The reasons for this phenomenon are numerous.

One of the basic assumptions of set theory is the axiom of infinity which says that there exist infinite sets. This assumption implies that the scale of infinite cardinals is itself infinite. Thus the axiom of infinity leads us out of the mathematical domains which are close to everyday practice and even to scientific experience. We are thus faced at the very beginning of set theory with the fundamental question of the philosophy of mathematics: which mathematical objects are admissible and why?

The same question arises in connection with sets of small powers, *e.g.*, with sets of integers. One could accept the "Platonistic" attitude and declare that sets (of integers) exist in the same sense as any other objects and that there is thus no arbitrariness in this notion. But even a Platonist must make it clear how he discovers properties of these allegedly existing objects. The adversaries of Platonism seek a solution by accepting one or another form of constructivism. This attitude is often more satisfactory philosophically than Platonism but unfortunately usually destructive for mathematics and even for those parts of it which are well established by the scientific praxis.

Most mathematicians do not perceive the problem which is posed by the abstractness of set theory. They prefer to take an aloof attitude and pretend not to be interested in philosophical (as opposed to purely mathematical) questions. In practice this simply means that they limit themselves to deducing theorems from axioms which were proposed by some authorities.

Interesting though the philosophical questions of foundations of set theory undoubtedly are, we shall not deal with them any further here since, for the reason just explained, the writings of contemporary set theorists and logicians do not offer very much which could help us in solving these problems. The writings of the period 1930—1964 which we are analyzing do not contain much philosophical discussion. These writings contain however great wealth of formal meta-mathematical results which we will try to summarize.

The best known results of this kind are connected with the axiom of choice and the continuum hypothesis. Many less famous but not less important problems are connected with other axioms or hypotheses of set theory *e.g.* with Suslin's hypothesis.

In this lecture we shall report on some of these problems and their solutions.

The Zermelo—Fraenkel and Bernays—Gödel axioms of set theory. The first axiomatic system of set theory was due to Zermelo. It was perfected soon afterwards by Fraenkel. In the period between 1930—1960 various new axiomatic systems of set theory were proposed. The best known is the system formulated by Bernays [5] and used by Gödel in his famous book [59]. The Bernays—Gödel system has three primitive notions: set, class, and ϵ, whereas Zermelo and Fraenkel used but two: set and ϵ. The distinction between sets and classes goes back to the writings of Cantor who distinguished between "consistent" and "inconsistent" sets.

The introduction of the new primitive notion allowed Bernays and Gödel to present the system of set theory in the form of a finitely axiomatizable system (the basic idea of this reduction was due to von Neumann); the previous systems and in particular the system of Zermelo required an infinite number of axioms.

The comparison of the Bernays—Gödel and Zermelo—Fraenkel set theories led to various discoveries.

Novak [156] showed that sentences provable in the Gödel—Bernays system and not containing the predicate "class" coincide with sentences provable in the Zermelo—Fraenkel system. We express this by saying that the Gödel—Bernays system is an inessential extension of the Zermelo—Fraenkel system. Also the consistency of the Gödel—Bernays system is reducible (in a finitistic way) to that of the Zermelo—Fraenkel system (Novak [156], Shoenfield [202]). Kleene [103] showed that each axiomatic system with a recursively enumerable set of axioms can be extended in an inessential way to a finitely axiomatizable system by adding one new primitive predicate (*cf.* also Vaught—Craig [26]). All these results show that the difference between both systems is not very great as far as their mathematical contents is concerned. The Zermelo—Fraenkel system was shown not to be finitely axiomatizable by Montague [144], [145]. Earlier attempts to obtain this result which were undertaken by Wang [241] and Mostowski [150] contained mistakes. The impossibility of a finite axiomatization of Peano's arithmetic and some other theories was proved (by using non-standard models) by Ryll—Nardzewski [189]; cf. also Hauschild [74].

Various extensions of both the Bernays—Gödel and the Zermelo—Fraenkel set theories were proposed in order to secure the existence of high cardinalities. The first step was made by Tarski [224] who formulated an axiom which secures the existence of inaccessible cardinals. Lévy [122] made the next step and formulated axiom schemata which secure the existence of various kinds of inaccessible cardinals. Lévy's schemata have the form of reflexion-principles and state, roughly speaking, that if the universe possesses a property expressed by a set theoretical formula, then there is a set in which this formula is also satisfied and which is closed with respect to operations described in the set-theoretical axioms.

These extensions of Zermelo—Fraenkel (or Bernays—Gödel) set theory are essential; adding Lévy's schemata we are able to prove statements which were formerly not provable. Such statements can even be found among statements concerning integers.

No relative consistency proof for the new axioms exists; its existence is excluded by Gödel's second undecidability theorem. Nevertheless set theoreticians believe that these axioms are consistent and this belief is strengthened by the fact that none of the known antinomies have appeared in the extended systems.

A very strong form of the axiom of infinity states that there are compact regular ordinals $\mu > 0$. This axiom is much stronger than Lévy's schemata. Nothing can be said as yet with regard to its consistency.

Other axiomatic systems of set theory. The Zermelo—Fraenkel (and Bernays—Gödel) set theory arose from attempts to formulate in a consistent way the intuitive assumptions of the naive (Cantorian) set theory. Cantor in the early phase of his work used implicitly the following axiom (axiom schema) of set existence: Whenever F is a formula (with one free variable x), there is a set S consisting of all elements a satisfying F. The same schema was explicitly used by Frege. Since the schema is known to be inconsistent one tried to modify it. The axioms of set theory represent an outcome of these endeavours.

Three ways of modifying the inconsistent principle of set existence were proposed:

(i)   One does not accept the principle for all formulae F;

(ii) One restricts the variability of a;

(iii) One imposes simultaneously both limitations (i) and (ii).

The simple type theory as first formulated by Chwistek and Ramsay accepts (iii). In this theory we admit only formulae which conform to the rules of formation prescribed by the theory. Moreover each variable has its prescribed domain (*cf.* Church [19] for an exact presentation of the syntax of the simple type theory). The Zermelo—Fraenkel and Bernays—Gödel systems accept (ii) because the schema of set existence accepted in these theories is the following: If S is a set, then so is $\{a : (a \in S) \land F(a)\}$. The restriction (i) is represented by axiomatic systems due to Quine [164] in which the set existence schema is assumed only for so-called stratified formulae whereas no limitation for the domains of variables is assumed. Quine's theory was extensively studied by a number of logicians (*e.g.* Wang [243]) but does not seem to have influenced the work of mathematicians.

It is more than probable that the axioms of set theory have not yet reached their definitive form. In connection with this question one should read the profound article of Gödel [61].

Axiom of choice. This axiom was from the start treated with distrust by many outstanding mathematicians. The philosophical discussion concerning its acceptability was closed well before 1930. In the period between 1930 and 1960 one obtained far-reaching formal results concerning the (relative) consistency and independence of the axiom. The first problem was dealt with in lecture IX. The problem of independence was essentially solved already in 1920 by Fraenkel though not in an entirely precise way. His method, usually called the permutation method, is applicable only to some systems of axiomatic set theory, *e.g.* to the Zermelo—Fraenkel system with the axiom of extensionality in the form

$$Z(x) \land Z(y) \land \bigwedge_s [(s \in x) \equiv (s \in y)] \to (x = y),$$

(where $Z(x)$ means: x is a set)

but is not applicable to the Zermelo—Fraenkel system with the additional axiom $\bigwedge_x Z(x)$ or any other axiom fixing the number of objects which are not sets. This shows how limited is the field of applications of the permutation method.

The general idea of the permutation method is this: we start from an infinite set K_0 whose elements are not sets and form new sets by repeating the operations of summation and of forming the power set. In this way we construct sets K_0, $K_1 = K_0 \cup P(K_0)$, $K_2 = K_0 \cup P(K_0) \cup P(K_0 \cup P(K_0))$ etc. This sequence can be extended into the transfinite. Each permutation π of K_0 acts on sets in each K_ξ and determines a permutation of this set. Let G be a group of permutations of K_0 and L a lattice of subsets K_0 containing all finite subsets of K_0 and consider only those elements x of K_ξ which have the following property (P): there is a set $X \in L$ such that each permutation π of K_0 which belongs to G and is constant on X leaves x invariant. The class of x which hereditarily have the property (P) is a model for Zermelo—Fraenkel axioms, with the possible exception of the axiom of choice.

Choosing a suitable group G and a suitable lattice L one obtains models by means of which it is possible to obtain independence proofs of various set-theoretical statements and in particular to prove the independence of the axiom of choice.

The literature dealing with these proofs is rather extensive. We refer to the synthetic paper of Lévy [123] as well as the newest additions to the theory obtained by Halpern [72] and Läuchli [121].

Specker [214], Mendelson [143] and Shoenfield [203] have modified the permutation method by considering instead of K_0 a family of sets x with the property $x \in x$. Their method is again applicable only to such set theories in which one can assume without inconsistency that there is an infinite set of such sets.

Cohen's notion of forcing. In 1963 Cohen [24] found a new method which allowed him to establish the independence of the axiom of choice and of the generalized continuum hypothesis from practically every system of set theory built along the Zermelo—Fraenkel lines. The success of his method is due to a new meta-mathematical notion of forcing.

We shall describe briefly this notion.

Let J be a first-order language with finitely many predicates and with infinitely many constants. We do not exclude the possibility that the variables and constants are divided in mutually exclusive types so that only such substitutions are admissible in which a variable is replaced by a constant of the same type. For the present we assume that J does not contain symbols for functions.

Forcing is a relation between a finite consistent sequence P of atomic sentences (*i.e.* atomic formulae without free variables) or negations of such sentences and a sentence F. We call P an "information". An information Q obtained from P by adding new terms to it is called an extension of P. We write then $P \prec Q$.

The definition proceeds by induction on the number of logical constants of F. In order to abbreviate our formulae we shall write $P \Vdash F$ instead of "P forces F".

1. If F is an atomic sentence, then $P \Vdash F$ if and only if F is a term of P.

2. If F is the sentence $F_1 \wedge F_2$ (or $F_1 \vee F_2$) then $P \Vdash F$ if and only if $P \Vdash F_1$ and (or) $P \Vdash F_2$.

3. If F is the sentence $F_1 \rightarrow F_2$, then $P \Vdash F$ if and only if every extension Q of P which satisfies $Q \Vdash F_1$ satisfies also $Q \Vdash F_2$.

4. If F is the sentence $\neg F_1$, then $P \Vdash F$ if and only if no extension Q of P satisfies $Q \Vdash F_1$.

5. If F is the sentence $\bigvee_x F_1$, then $P \Vdash F$ if and only if there is a constant a (of the same type as x) such that $P \Vdash F(a)$.

6. If F is the sentence $\bigwedge_x F_1$, then $P \Vdash F$ if and only if no extension Q of P and no constant a (of the same type as x) satisfies the condition $Q \Vdash \neg F_1(a)$.

Condition 6 can be rephrased thus: for every constant a (of the appropriate type) and every extension Q of P an extension R of Q can be found such that $R \Vdash F_1(a)$.

Most characteristic are conditions 4 and 6. Condition 4 secures that once we have the relation $P \Vdash \neg F_1$, then no matter how we extend P to Q we shall never encounter the situation when we would have to assume $Q \Vdash F_1$. Similarly condition 6 secures that once we have $P \Vdash \bigwedge_x F_1$, we shall never have the relation $Q \Vdash \neg F_1(a)$ whatever a and whatever extension Q of P we choose. Thus if we imagine the sequence P growing as time goes on, then the fact that a relation $P \Vdash \neg F_1$ (or $P \Vdash \bigwedge_x F_1(x)$) holds at a given moment prevents relations of the form $Q \Vdash F_1$ (or $Q \Vdash \neg F_1(a)$) to hold in the future (independently of the way we extended P).

The definition of forcing is interesting quite apart from its applications. Feferman [38] investigated it in the case of a formal system of Peano arithmetic with an additional one place predicate and showed that it is hyper-arithmetical. Grzegorczyk [70] showed that if one considers only sentences without quantifiers, then the sentences F

10

which are forced by every information P coincide with theorems of
the intuitionistic propositional calculus. No such simple characterization is known for arbitrary sentences.

In the case considered by Cohen the language J contained not only
constants and variables but also symbols of functions. In order to
describe his construction we must go back to the construction of
Gödel [60]. Modifying inessentially our definitions from lecture IX
we define a transfinite sequence K_μ of sets such that $K_0 = \omega =$ set
of all integers, $K_\lambda = \bigcup_{\xi < \lambda} K_\xi$ for limit numbers λ and K_{a+1} is the
family of all sets of the form $\{a : (a \in K_a) \wedge \models_{\boldsymbol{M}_a} F[a\,;\,b_1, \ldots, b_k]\}$
where F is a formula with $k + 1$ free variables, $b_1, \ldots, b_k \in K_a$
and $\boldsymbol{M}_a = \,<K_a, \epsilon_a>$ is the model with the universe K_a and with
the ϵ-relation limited to K_a.

It follows from Gödel's proof that there is a denumerable ordinal
a_0 such that $\boldsymbol{M}_{a_0}$ is a model of set theory (with the axiom of constructibility and hence with the axiom of choice and the generalized
continuum hypothesis). Cohen's plan was now to add to $\boldsymbol{M}_{a_0}$ a new
set C of integers and close $K_{a_0} \cup \{C\}$ with respect to all operations
φ used in the construction of K_{a_0}. He hoped to achieve by a suitable
choice of C that C will not be a constructible set in the new model.
In order to obtain a model in which the continuum hypothesis does
not hold he adjoined to $\boldsymbol{M}_{a_0}$ a sequence $C = \{C_\delta\}$ of new sets of
integers such that no two terms of C are identical and δ ranges over
the ordinal ω_2 (or ω_3, or ω_4, ...) of the model $\boldsymbol{M}_{a_0}$. Of course the
ordinal ω_2 of the model $\boldsymbol{M}_{a_0}$ is denumerable (although this ordinal
satisfies in the model the formula "x is non-denumerable"). It is not
immediately obvious that a choice of C (or $\{C_\delta\}$) is possible: If we
add to $\boldsymbol{M}_{a_0}$ an arbitrary C and close it with respect to the operations
φ we will usually not obtain a model for set theory. Even if we are
lucky enough and obtain such a model it will usually not have the
property (needed in the proof of independence of the continuum
hypothesis) which says that if an element ω_2 satisfies in $\boldsymbol{M}_{a_0}$ the
formula: "x is the second uncountable ordinal" then the same
element ω_2 satisfies this formula in the new model. Thus the appropriate choice of C is the essential point of the whole proof. Cohen
achieved it by his theory of forcing. He considered a language in
which there are variables and constants of types τ where τ ranges
over ordinals $< a_0$. To each element a in K_{a_0} there is a constant of
type τ denoting a. In addition there is a constant c denoting a set of
integers (or constants c_δ denoting sets of integers and a constant c

for the whole sequence $\{c_\delta\}$) and symbols for the operations φ. Besides these symbols we admit unrestricted variables without any limitations of range. Sentences in which no unrestricted variables occur are called limited, other unlimited. A restricted sentence F has a rank which is defined as the least ordinal ξ such that no constant and no variable of type $\geq \xi$ occurs in F. Informations P contain only sentences of the form $n \in c$ or $n \,\bar{\epsilon}\, c$ (and $n \in c_\delta$ or $n \,\bar{\epsilon}\, c_\delta$ respectively).

We first define the relation of forcing for limited sentences. Conditions 2—6 remain unchanged but 1 is modified unless F is an atomic formula of the form allowed in P. In other cases the atomic formula $a \in b$ possesses a structure which allows us to reduce the relation $P \Vdash a \in b$ to simpler cases.

We shall illustrate the definition in two cases:

Let b be the constant $\{x : (x \in K_a) \wedge \models_{M_a} F(x, b_1, \ldots, b_k)\}$ and a a constant for an element of K_a. In this case the relation $P \Vdash a \in b$ is defined as $P \Vdash F_a (a, b_1, \ldots, b_k)$ where F_a is a limited statement obtained from F by replacing all unrestricted variables by variables of type a. If b is a constant for an element of K_a and a the constant $\{x : (x \in K_a) \wedge \models_{M_a} F(x, b_1, \ldots, b_k)\}$ then $P \Vdash a \in b$ holds if and only if $P \Vdash \bigwedge_{x_a} [(a = x_a) \wedge (x_a \in b)]$ which in turn can be reduced by the use of rule 5 and by the definition of equation to relations of the form $P \Vdash G$ where G has a rank less than a.

The remarks we made should be sufficient to illustrate how we can define the relation of forcing for limited sentences by the use of transfinite induction.

This definition being completed we define forcing for unlimited sentences by the rules 1—6. No complication arises in case of atomic sentences since they are all limited sentences and hence forcing is defined for them.

Starting from the definition of forcing it is easy to prove (non-constructively) that there is an infinite increasing sequence $P_1 \prec P_2 \prec \ldots$ of informations with the following properties:

(1) for each sentence F either F or $\neg F$ is eventually forced;

(2) for each n either $n \in c$ or $\neg (n \in c)$ (and for each n and δ either $n \in c_\delta$ or $\neg (n \in c_\delta)$) eventually occurs in the sequence.

Each sequence with the properties (1) and (2) determines a set C of integers (or a sequence $\{C_\delta\}$ of such sets). We define C as the set of such n that the formula $n \, \epsilon \, c$ eventually occurs in the sequence $P_1, P_2, \ldots$ (similarly C_δ is the set of integers n such that the formula $n \, \epsilon \, c_\delta$ eventually occurs in the sequence $P_1, P_2, \ldots$).

Sets C (or C_δ) defined in this way are called generic.

Cohen showed in his independence proofs that if one adjoins to M_{a_0} any generic set C (or any sequence of such sets) and closes the resulting set with respect to the operations φ, then one obtains a model in which the axiom of constructibility (or the continuum hypothesis) is not valid. The details of this proof are too involved to be given here.

Similar construction allowed Cohen and other mathematicians working with the method of forcing to obtain other proofs of independence. *E.g.* Cohen showed that if the system of Zermelo—Fraenkel without the axiom of choice is consistent, then it remains consistent after adjunction of an axiom stating that there is a denumerable set S of pairs each element of which is a set of real numbers and such that there is no choice set for S.

The main advantage of Cohen's method as compared with the permutation method is that it is applicable not only to the Zermelo—Fraenkel (or Gödel—Bernays) set theory but also to most theories obtained from them by the adjunction of axioms of infinity which we discussed earlier and of axioms which determine the number of non-sets. Thus only now, after this method was created, can we consider the independence problems as solved.

Properties of generic sets. Besides solving the independence problem, Cohen's method suggested many new problems. The most interesting is the study of generic sets. These sets seem to satisfy (with respect to a given model M_{a_0}) intuitions which underlie Brouwer's intuitionistic conception of a set (of integers). There is no way to define (in a given language) any such set individually; we can only give information concerning any finite number of individual members of such a set. The work on these sets is in full progress. We shall quote only one result obtained by Cohen: he showed that the family of generic sets is very big. In fact this family is of second category in the Baire space of all sets of integers.

The notion of a generic set can be defined not only for set theory but also for arithmetic and other theories. Ryll—Nardzewski (in an unpublished paper) considered topological properties of generic sets. He proved that if F is an arithmetical formula with a parameter Z ranging over generic sets, then the truth-value of F is a continuous function of Z. This theorem allowed him to characterize the family of generic sets and to prove that it is of second category without recourse to the notion of forcing.

The same results can probably be obtained for set theory but no definite proof exists as yet.

Final remarks. The philosophical importance of set theory is obvious: the fundamental epistemological questions connected with mathematics can be best illustrated on set-theoretical problems. The most fundamental question is, of course, how to decide between the formalistic and "Platonistic" conceptions of the abstract parts of mathematics. (In the case of the less abstract parts the problem is not as acute, because we understand the way in which needs of practical life and of science formed the mathematical theories.)

Cohen's work did not create these philosophical questions. They existed long before meta-mathematics was created. Still the rigorous proof that there are two consistent and mutually incompatible set theories stirred the imagination of many mathematicians who were formerly indifferent to these questions. It is at present hard to tell whether mathematics will accept the existence of these two incompatible set theories or will try to find new axioms which will eliminate one of them or finally will try to limit mathematics to more finitistic domains. We see that the issue between Platonists, formalists and intuitionists is as undecided to-day as it was fifty years ago.

Lecture XVI

On direct and reduced products

We devote this lecture to a rather special algebraic construction which proved of great value in solving various problems of mathematical logic.

The direct product. Let I be a set $\neq 0$ and let $\boldsymbol{M}_i = \,<\!A_i, R_i\!>$ for i in I be a model in which A_i is a non-void set and R_i a binary relation. The restriction to models of this special type is not essential: the models $\boldsymbol{M}_i$ could be *any* models as long as they all are of the same type, *i.e.* the number of relations must be the same in all the models $\boldsymbol{M}_i$ and if $R_{i_1}, R_{i_2}, \ldots$ are relations of $\boldsymbol{M}_i$ then the number of arguments in R_{ik} must be equal to the number of arguments of R_{jk} for arbitrary i, j in I.

The direct product of the models $\boldsymbol{M}_i$ is the model $\boldsymbol{P} = \boldsymbol{P}_{i \in I} \, \boldsymbol{M}_i = \,<\!A, R\!>$ where $A = \boldsymbol{P}_{i \in I} \, A_i$ is the set of all functions f with domain I satisfying the condition $f(i) \in A_i$ for $i \in I$ and R is a binary relation defined thus:

(1) $$f \, R \, g = \bigwedge_{i \in I} [f(i) \, R_i \, g(i)].$$

In the case when all $\boldsymbol{M}_i$ are equal to a model $\boldsymbol{M}$ we denote $\boldsymbol{P}_{i \in I} \, \boldsymbol{M}_i$ by $\boldsymbol{M}^I$ and call it the direct power of $\boldsymbol{M}$.

This standard algebraic construction has been generalized by Feferman and Vaught [40] and applied to several decision problems. In the generalized notion which they introduced the relation R depends not only of the relations R_i but of some auxiliary relations defined in I.

The reduced direct product. This product is a special case of the notion introduced by Feferman and Vaught but we shall define it directly. Let F be a maximal filter in the Boolean algebra of the family of all subsets of I. This filter determines an equivalence relation $\sim$ in the set A:

$$f \sim g \equiv \left\{ i \in I : f(i) = g(i) \right\} \in F.$$

The relation $\sim$ is compatible with R, *i.e.*

$$(f \sim g) \wedge (f' \sim g') \to [fRg \equiv f'Rg'],$$

hence we can form the quotient system $P/\!\!\sim = <A/\!\!\sim, R/\!\!\sim>$ whose universe is the set $A/\!\!\sim$ of all equivalence classes $f/\!\!\sim = \left\{ g : g \sim f \right\}$ and whose relation $R/\!\!\sim$ is defined by the equivalence

$$(f/\!\!\sim) \; R/\!\!\sim \; (g/\!\!\sim) \equiv fRg$$

The model $<A/\!\!\sim, R/\!\!\sim>$ is called the reduced product of the M_i. It depends of course on the filter F.

The form of the definition given above is due to Tarski (*cf.* [43]) who obtained it by simplifying a much more involved definition proposed by Łoś [128]. Łoś's construction, though no more in use at present, is worth mentioning if only for its connections with many-valued logics. Łoś considered the set $\left\{ i \in I : f(i) = g(i) \right\}$ as a kind of "distance" of two functions f and g and considered the direct product $P_i M_i$ as a special case of a "logical space" which insofar differs from the usual models as the values of atomic formulae aRb are not merely the truth values $\mathfrak{F}$, $\mathfrak{B}$ but elements of an arbitrary Boolean algebra. Identifying suitably elements of a "logical space" Łoś arrived at what we call now reduced products.

The essential property of reduced products (discovered already by Łoś [128]) is expressed by the equivalence.

(2) $\models_{P/\sim} H[f_1/\!\!\sim, \ldots, f_k/\!\!\sim] \equiv \left\{ i \in I : \models_{M_i} H[f_1(i), \ldots, f_k(i)] \right\} \in F$

in which H is an arbitrary first-order formula with one binary predicate and possibly the identity symbol and with k free variables.

The proof of (2) is very easy and uses induction with respect to the number of logical connectives in H.

It follows from (2) that

(3) $M^I/\!\!\sim$ is elementarily equivalent with M.

The model $M^I/\!\!\sim$ contains a sub-model isomorphic with M namely the sub-model consisting of equivalence classes $f/\!\!\sim$ where f is a constant function. Identifying M with this sub-model we obtain from (2)

(4) $M^I/\!\!\sim$ is an elementary extension of M.

If F is a principal filter $F = \left\{ X \subset I : i_0 \in X \right\}$ where i_0 is a fixed element of I, then the reduced product $P_{i \in I} M_i/\!\!\sim$ is isomorphic with M_{i_0} and the whole construction is trivial. Thus the only interesting case is when the filter F is non-principal.

Compactness theorem. The first striking application of the reduced direct products was the following simple proof of the compactness theorem (see Frayne—Morel—Scott [43]):

Let X be a set of sentences such that each finite subset of X is satisfiable. We want to prove that there is a model in which all sentences of X are true.

In order to obtain this result by the use of reduced products let I be the family of all finite subsets of X and denote, for $i \in I$ by M_i a model in which all sentences belonging to i are true. For arbitrary sentences $S_1, \ldots, S_k$ in X we denote by $J(S_1, \ldots, S_k)$ the family of sets $i \in I$ such that $(S_1 \in i) \wedge \ldots \wedge (S_k \in i)$. It is obvious that all the families $J(S_1, \ldots, S_k)$ (where $S_1, \ldots, S_k$ range over X and k over arbitrary positive integers) form a filter F_0 in the Boolean algebra of all subsets of I and $0 \,\bar{\in}\, F_0$. We extend this filter to a maximal filter F not containing 0. The required model in which all the sentences of X are valid is the reduced product $P = P_{i \in I} \, M_i/\sim$.

Indeed if $S \in X$, then the set $\{i \in I : S \in i\}$ belongs to F_0 and hence to F whence, by (2), S is true in P.

Another theorem which can be proved in the same way is this: if every finite subset j of a model M can be extended to a model M_j which belongs to a given elementary class K, then the whole M can be so extended.

Both these results can be obtained by an application of Gödel's completeness theorem. The proofs using reduced products are more direct and hence give a better insight in the structure of the models whose existence is stated in the theorems.

Other, deeper applications of the reduced products were mentioned in lecture XIII.

Applications to the abstract set theory. Let us assume that for each i in I the relation R_i orders the universe A_i of M_i. It follows from (2) that the universe of the reduced product $P = P_{i \in I} \, M_i/\sim$ is ordered by the relation $R/\sim$. If the R_i are well-orderings, then, as simple examples show, P need not be well-ordered. However, the following theorem is true:

(5) If F is a σ-multiplicative filter (*i.e.* if $X_n \in F$ for $n = 0, 1, 2, \ldots$ implies $\bigcap_n X_n \in F$), then the reduced product of well-ordered models is itself well-ordered.

Theorem (5) is a basis of all results concerning denumerably additive filters in Boolean algebras of all subsets of a set. We shall show this by sketching the proof (due to Keisler [91]) that the first inaccessible non-denumerable cardinal $\aleph_a$ is not measurable, *i.e.* that there is no non-trivial denumerably multiplicative maximal filter F in the Boolean algebra of all subsets of a set X of power $\aleph_a$.

Let us assume that such a filter F exists and that X is the set of all ordinal $< \omega_a$ ordered by the $\leq$ relation. It can then be shown that F is $\aleph_\lambda$-multiplicative for each $\lambda < \alpha$. According to (5) the reduced power $X^X/\sim$ determined by F is well-ordered. The set $X^X/\sim$ contains a subset similar to X consisting of equivalence classes $f/\sim$ where f is constant. This subset which we shall identify with X can be shown to be a segment of $X^X/\sim$. If F were a principal filter then $X^X/\sim$ and X would be isomorphic. Otherwise the order type of $X^X/\sim$ is greater than X since *e.g.* the equivalence class of the identity function $\delta(x) = x$ does not belong to X. Let $\varphi/\sim$ be the first equivalence class in $X^X/\sim$ after X and consider the sets:

$$A = \{x : \varphi(x) \text{ has an immediate predecessor } \varphi^*(x)\},$$

$$B = \{x : \varphi(x) \text{ has no predecessor and there is an ordinal}$$
$$\xi < \varphi(x) \text{ such that } \overline{\varphi(x)} \leq 2^{\bar{\xi}}\},$$

$$C = \{x : (\varphi(x) \text{ has no predecessor}) \wedge \bigwedge_{\xi < \varphi(x)} (\overline{\varphi(x)} > 2^{\bar{\xi}})\}$$

(we denote as usual by $\bar{\xi}$ the cardinal number of the set $\{\eta : \eta < \xi\}$). Since $X = A \cup B \cup C$ one at least of the sets A, B, C is in F. If $A \in F$, then putting $\psi(x) = \varphi^*(x)$ for $x \in A$ and $\psi(x) = 0$ otherwise we obtain a function ψ such that $\psi/\sim$ precedes $\varphi/\sim$ in $X^X/\sim$. Hence ψ is a constant and so is φ. This contradiction shows that $A \bar{\in} F$.

If $B \in F$, then we denote by $\psi(x)$ the smallest $\xi < \varphi(x)$ such that $\overline{\varphi(x)} \leq 2^{\bar{\xi}}$ and infer similarly that φ is a constant, which is impossible.

Finally if $C \in F$, then for each x in C there must exist an ordinal $\lambda(x) < \varphi(x)$ such that $\varphi(x)$ is co-final with $\lambda(x)$, since $\varphi(x)$ is smaller than the first inaccessible cardinal. Again we show that λ is a constant function, $\lambda(x) = \lambda_0$. Hence $\varphi(x) = \lim_{\xi < \lambda_0} \vartheta(x, \xi)$ for all $x \in C$.

For each fixed $\xi < \lambda_0$ the function ϑ considered as a function of

x alone has values $< \varphi(x)$, whence it is a constant, $\vartheta(x, \xi) = \gamma(\xi)$ on a set Q_ξ which belongs to F. The intersection $D = \cap_{\xi < \lambda_0} Q_\xi \cap C$ belongs to F and for x in D we have $\vartheta(x, \xi) = \gamma(\xi)$. It follows that for x in D the equation $\varphi(x) = lim_{\xi < \lambda_0} \vartheta(x, \xi) = lim_{\xi < \lambda_0} \gamma(\xi)$ is true whence we infer that φ is equal to a constant on a set which belongs to F. This however contradicts the definition of φ.

Hence we obtain a contradiction in all cases. This shows that the filter F with the properties we enumerated cannot exist.

By using a similar argument Scott [198] proved that if there is a non-trivial maximal denumerably multiplicative filter F in the Boolean algebra of a set X, then F is non-constructible. The most recent results (Gaifman [49]) show that under the same assumption for any infinite λ there are no more than $\bar{\lambda}$ constructible subsets of $\{\xi : \xi < \lambda\}$. In particular there are only denumerably many constructible sets of integers provided that measurable cardinals exist! This result was obtained before Gaifman by Rawbotten.

Applications of reduced products to non-standard models of arithmetic. Let $\boldsymbol{M}_0$ be the model $<\omega, \Sigma, \Pi>$ where ω is the set of integers and Σ, Π are the relations $x = y + z$, $x = y \cdot z$. We call $\boldsymbol{M}_0$ the standard model of arithmetic.

For every infinite set I and every non-trivial maximal filter F the reduced power $\boldsymbol{M}_0^I/\sim$ is by (2) elementarily equivalent to $\boldsymbol{M}_0$ but is not isomorphic to $\boldsymbol{M}_0$ since the equivalence class of the diagonal function is different from the values of all numerals in $\boldsymbol{M}_0^I/\sim$. Using the downward Skolem—Löwenheim theorem we can obtain from $\boldsymbol{M}_0^I/\sim$ a denumerable non-standard model elementarily equivalent to $\boldsymbol{M}_0$. In this way we have a simple method of constructing non-standard models.

Scott [196] modified this method by showing that one obtains a non-standard denumerable model by limiting from the start the family $\boldsymbol{P} A_i$. He considered the set D of functions definable in $\boldsymbol{M}_0$ and a maximal non-trivial filter F in the Boolean algebra of definable subsets of $\boldsymbol{M}_0$ (the existence of this filter can be established without the axiom of choice which is necessary when one wants to prove the existence of a maximal non-trivial filter in the Boolean algebra of all subsets of an infinite set). Repeating the construction of the reduced power but including in it only equivalence classes of definable functions, Scott obtained a non-standard denumerable model elementarily equivalent to $\boldsymbol{M}_0$. He also showed that this model is isomorphic with a model constructed by Skolem [209]. The method used by Skolem, while formally different from the method of reduced powers, is thus essentially equivalent to the latter.

Scott's analysis showed that one does not obtain a model if one replaces D by a more restricted set, *e.g.* the set of polynomials or of recursive functions. These negative results showed that it is not easy to construct effective examples of non-standard models. We should mention here results (obtained among others by Feferman [35], Scott [196], these authors jointly with Tennenbaum [39], and Rabin [167]) which show that there are no recursive non-standard models satisfying the axioms of Peano. All these results explain why it is so difficult to establish the independence of number-theoretical sentences from the arithmetical axioms by the use of non-standard models: In order to find such applications one should have a much better knowledge of the structure of these models and more direct methods of their constructions than we have at present.

Of other works on non-standard models we here mention an important paper by Specker—MacDowell [132] who used the method of Skolem to establish the following theorem: every model M of Peano's axioms can be extended to a model M' in such a way that M' is an elementary extension of M and all elements of $M'-M$ are greater than the elements of M. Another promising direction of the studies of non-standard models seems to be one concerned with automorphisms of such models (*cf.* Ehrenfeucht—Mostowski [31]).

Non-standard models for analysis. The method of reduced products can be used to obtain non-standard models for an arbitrary theory. A. Robinson investigated such models in a series of papers (see for instance [182], [183]). The theory which he considered is very rich and contains symbols for all functions and relations defined in the set of real numbers. Axioms of the theory are all sentences true for real numbers. Robinson showed that this theory admits non-standard models. He himself constructed these models by the use of the extended completeness theorem. Other writers prefer to construct them by the use of reduced products.

Each non-standard model for Robinson's theory is a non-archimedean field R^* which is an elementary extension of the field R of real numbers. Each function f defined on R has an extension f^* which is defined on R^* and each first-order property of f is preserved by the extension.

The field R^* contains actually infinitely small and actually infinitely great elements, *i.e.* elements a, A such that $0 < |a| < 1/n$

and $|A| > n$ for each integer n. It is thus possible to derive in R^* the basic theorems of analysis using the Leibnizian ideas of infinitesimals. Thus *e.g.* we call a function f continuous at the point x if $f(x + a) - f(x)$ is infinitely small for each infinitely small number a. A derivative of f at the point x is a number d such that the difference $\{[f(x + a) - f(x)]/a\} - d$ is infinitely small for each infinitesimal a. Robinson showed that one obtains in this way a completely rigourous theory which is formally identical with the classical analysis. It is at present not clear, whether the non-standard analysis will bring essentially new results. It is nevertheless remarkable that we can give a clear and precise presentation of ideas which were considered obscure for almost 300 years.

*   *   *

We stop here our presentation of what we consider as the most important results in the recent development of logic and the foundations of mathematics. The rate of development of these domains is presently so rapid that many new excellent results will certainly appear before these lectures will come to the hands of prospective readers. Let us hope that these new results will not only bring new interesting insights into the details but also allow us to form a sound judgment about the outstanding problems in the philosophy of mathematics which have been waiting so long for a final solution.

Bibliography

[1] J. W. Addison. **On some points of the theory of recursive functions.** Unpublished dissertation Univ. of Wisconsin 1954.

[2] J. W. Addison. *Separation principles in the hierarchies of the classical and effective descriptive set theory.* **Fundamenta Mathematicae,** vol. 46 (1958—59), pp. 123—135.

[3] J. W. Addison. *Some consequences of the axiom of constructibility.* **Fundamenta Mathematicae,** vol. 46 (1958—59), pp. 337—357.

[3 a] J. W. Addison. *Some problems in hierarchy theory.* **Recursive function theory. Proceedings of Symposia in Pure Mathematics,** vol. V. American Mathematical Society, Providence, R. I., 1962, pp. 123—130.

[4] G. Asser. *Das Repräsentantenproblem im Prädikatenkalkül der ersten Stufe mit Identität.* **Zeitschrift für mathematische Logik und Grundlagen der Mathematik,** vol. 1 (1955), pp. 252—263.

[5] P. Bernays. *A system of axiomatic set theory I, II.* **Journal of Symbolic Logic,** vol. 2 (1937), pp. 65—77, and vol. 6 (1941), pp. 1—17.

[6] E. W. Beth. *On Padoa's method in the theory of definition.* **Indagationes Mathematicae** vol. 15 (1953), pp. 330—339.

[7] E. W. Beth. *Semantic entailment and formal derivability.* **Mededelingen der Koninklijke Nederlandse Akademie van Wetenschappen, Afd. Letterkunde,** n.s., vol. 18 (1955), pp. 309—342.

[8] E. W. Beth. *Semantic construction of intuitionistic logic.* **Mededelingen der Koninklijke Nederlandse Akademie van Wetenschappen, Afd. Letterkunde,** n.s., vol. 19 (1956), pp. 357—388.

[9] W. W. Boone. *Certain simple, unsolvable problems of group theory V—VI.* **Indagationes Mathematicae,** vol. 19 (1957), pp. 22—27 and 227—232.

[10] J. R. Büchi. *Weak second order arithmetic and finite automata.* **Zeitschrift für mathematische Logik und Grundlagen der Mathematik,** vol. 6 (1960), pp. 66—92.

[11] J. R. Büchi. *On a decision method in restricted second order arithmetic.* **Logic, Methodology and Philosophy of Science: Proceedings of the 1960 International Congress.** Stanford University Press, Stanford, California, 1962, pp. 1—11.

[12] J. R. Büchi. *Turing—Machines and the Entscheidungsproblem.* **Mathematische Annalen,** vol. 148 (1962), pp. 201—213.

[13] K. Chandrasekharan. *The logic of intuitionistic mathematics.* **The Mathematics Student** (Madras), vol. 9 (1942), pp. 143—154.

[14] C. C. Chang. *On unions of chains of models.* **Proceedings of the American Mathematical Society,** vol. 10 (1959), pp. 120—127.

[15] C. C. Chang. *Logic with positive and negative truth values.* **Modal and many-valued logics. Acta Philosophica Fennica,** vol. 16 (1963), pp. 19—39.

[16] A. Church. *A set of postulates for the foundation of logic (second paper).* **Annals of Mathematics,** vol. 34 (1933), pp. 839—864.

[17] A. Church. *A note on the Entscheidungsproblem.* **Journal of Symbolic Logic,** vol. 1 (1936), pp. 40—41 and 101—102.

[18] A. Church. *The constructive second number class.* **Bulletin of the American Mathematical Society,** vol. 44 (1938), pp. 224—232.

[19] A. Church. *A formulation of the simple theory of types.* **Journal of Symbolic Logic,** vol. 5 (1940), pp. 56—68.

[20] A. Church. *On the concept of a random sequence.* **Bulletin of the American Mathematical Society,** vol. 46 (1940), pp. 130—135.

[21] A. Church. *Application of recursive arithmetic to the problem of circuit synthesis.* **Summaries of talks presented at the Summer Institute for Symbolic Logic, Cornell University, 1957.** Second edition, Princeton University Press, Princeton, N. J., 1960, pp. 3—50.

[22] A. Church and S. C. Kleene. *Formal definitions in the theory of ordinal numbers.* **Fundamenta Mathematicae,** vol. 28 (1937), pp. 11—21

[23] P. J. Cohen. *A minimal model for set theory.* **Bulletin of the American Mathematical Society,** vol. 69 (1963), pp. 537—540.

[24] P. J. Cohen. *The independence of the continuum hypothesis I and II.* **Proceedings of the National Academy of the U.S.A.,** vol. 50 (1963), pp. 1143—1148, and vol. 51 (1964), pp. 105—110.

[25] W. Craig. *Linear reasoning. A new form of the Herbrand-Gentzen theorem.* **Journal of Symbolic Logic,** vol. 22 (1957), pp. 250—268.

[26] W. Craig and R. L. Vaught. *Finite axiomatizability using additional predicates.* **Journal of Symbolic Logic,** vol. 23 (1958), pp. 289—308.

[27] J. C. E. Dekker and J. Myhill. **Recursive equivalence types. University of California Publications in Mathematics,** vol. 3 (1960), pp. 67—214.

[28] B. Dreben, P. Andrews and S. Aanderaa. *False lemmas in Herbrand.* **Bulletin of the American Mathematical Society,** vol. 69 (1963), pp. 699—706.

[29] V. H. Dyson and G. Kreisel. **Analysis of Beth's semantic construction of intuitionistic logic** (mimeographed). Applied Mathematics and Statistics Laboratory, Stanford University, Stanford, California, 1961.

[30] A. Ehrenfeucht. *An application of games to the completeness problem for formalized theories.* **Fundamenta Mathematicae,** vol. 49 (1960—61), pp. 129—141.

[31] A. Ehrenfeucht and A. Mostowski. *Models of axiomatic theories admitting automorphisms.* **Fundamenta Mathematicae,** vol. 43 (1956), pp. 50—68.

[32] E. Engeler. *A characterization of theories with isomorphic denumerable models.* **Notices of the American Mathematical Society,** vol. 6 (1959), p. 161.

[33] S. Feferman. Review of [172]. **Journal of Symbolic Logic,** vol. 17 (1952), p. 72.

[34] S. Feferman. *Degrees of unsolvability associated with classes of formalized theories.* **Journal of Symbolic Logic,** vol. 22 (1957), pp. 161—175.

[35] S. Feferman. *Arithmetically definable models of formalized arithmetic.* **Notices of the American Mathematical Society,** vol. 5 (1958), pp. 679—680.

[36] S. Feferman. *Arithmetization of metamathematics in a general setting.* **Fundamenta Mathematicae,** vol. 49 (1960—61), pp. 35—92.

[37] S. Feferman. *Transfinite recursive progressions of axiomatic theories.* **Journal of Symbolic Logic,** vol. 27 (1962), pp. 259—316.

[38] S. Feferman. *Some applications of the method of forcing and generic sets.* **Fundamenta Mathematicae,** vol. 56 (1965), pp. 325—345.

[39] S. Feferman, D. Scott and S. Tennenbaum. *Models of arithmetic through function rings.* **Notices of the American Mathematical Society,** vol. 6 (1959), p. 173.

[40] S. Feferman and R. L. Vaught. *The first order properties of products of algebraic systems.* **Fundamenta Mathematicae,** vol. 47 (1959), pp. 57—103.

[41] R. Fraïssé. *Sur quelques classifications des relations basées sur des isomorphismes restraintes.* **Publications Scientifiques de l'Université d'Alger,** Série A (mathématiques), vol. 2 (1955), pp. 15—60 and 273—295.

[42] R. Fraïssé. *Sur une extension de la polyrelation et des parentés tirant son origine du calcul logiques du k-ème échelon.* **Le raisonnement en mathématiques et en sciences expérimentales. Colloques Internationaux du CNRS,** Paris, 1958, pp. 45—50.

[43] T. Frayne, A. C. Morel and D. S. Scott. *Reduced direct products.* **Fundamenta Mathematicae,** vol. 51 (1962), pp. 195—228.

[44] R. M. Friedberg. *Two recursively enumerable sets of incomparable degrees of unsolvability (solution of Post's problem 1944).* **Proceedings of the National Academy of Sciences of the U.S.A.,** vol. 43 (1957), pp. 236—238.

[45] R. M. Friedberg. *4 quantifier completeness: a Banach—Mazur functional not uniformly partial recursive.* **Bulletin de l'Académie Polonaise des Sciences,** série math., astr. et phys., vol. 6 (1958), pp. 1—5.

[46] R. M. Friedberg. *The existence of a maximal set.* **Summaries of talks presented at the Summer Institute for Symbolic Logic, Cornell University, 1957.** Second edition, Princeton University Press, Princeton, N. J. 1960, pp. 407—409.

[47] A. Fröhlich and J. C. Shepherdson. *Effective procedures in field theory.* **Philosophical Transactions of the Royal Society of London,** Series A, vol. 248 (1955—56), pp. 407—432.

[48] G. Fuhrken. *Skolem-type normal forms for first-order languages with a generalized quantifier.* **Fundamenta Mathematicae,** vol. 54 (1964), pp. 291—302.

[49] H. Gaifman. *Further consequences of the existence of measurable cardinals.* Forthcoming in the **Proceedings of the 1964 International Congress of Logic, Methodology, and Philosophy of Science in Jerusalem.** North-Holland Publishing Company, Amsterdam, 1965. Forthcoming.

[50] G. Gentzen. *Untersuchungen über das logische Schliessen.* **Mathematische Zeitschrift,** vol. 39 (1934), pp. 176—210, 405—431.

[51] G. Gentzen. *Die Widerspruchsfreiheit der reinen Zahlentheorie.* **Mathematische Annalen,** vol. 112 (1936), pp. 493—565.

[52] V. Glivenko. *Sur quelques points de la logique de M. Brouwer.* **Bulletin des Sciences de l'Académie Belgique,** série 5, vol. 15 (1929), pp. 183—188.

[53] K. Gödel. *Die Vollständigkeit der Axiome des logischen Funktionenkalküls.* **Monatshefte für Mathematik und Physik,** vol. 37 (1930), pp. 349—360.

[54] K. Gödel. *Über formal unentscheidbare Sätze der Principia Mathematica und verwandter Systeme I.* **Monatshefte für Mathematik und Physik,** vol. 38 (1931), pp. 173—198.

[55] K. Gödel. *Ein Spezialfall des Entscheidungsproblems der theoretischen Logik.* **Ergebnisse eines mathematischen Kolloquiums,** Heft 2 (1932), pp. 27—28.

[56] K. Gödel. *Zur intuitionistischen Arithmetik und Zahlentheorie.* **Ergebnisse eines mathematischen Kolloquiums,** Heft 4 (1933), pp. 34—38.

[57] K. Gödel. **On undecidable propositions of formal mathematical systems.** (Mimeographed.) Princeton 1934, 30 pp.

[58] K. Gödel. *Über die Länge von Beweisen.* **Ergebnisse eines mathematischen Kolloquiums,** Heft 7 (1936), pp. 23—24.

[59] K. Gödel. *The consistency of the axiom of choice and of the generalized continuum hypothesis.* **Proceedings of the National Academy of Sciences of the U.S.A.,** vol. 24 (1938), pp. 556—557.

[60] K. Gödel. **The consistency of the axiom of choice and of the generalized continuum hypothesis with the axioms of set theory.** Princeton Univ. Press, Princeton, N. J., 1940.

[61] K. Gödel. *What is Cantor's continuum problem?* **The American Mathematical Monthly,** vol., 54 (1947), pp. 515—525.

[62] K. Gödel. *Über eine bisher noch nicht benützte Erweiterung des finiten Standpunktes.* **Logica (Studia Paul Bernays dedicata).** Ed. Griffon, Neuchatel, 1959, pp. 76—83.

[63] R. L. Goodstein. **Recursive number theory.** North-Holland Publishing Company, Amsterdam 1957.

[64] R. L. Goodstein. **Recursive analysis.** North-Holland Publishing Company, Amsterdam 1961.

[65] A. Grzegorczyk. *Undecidability of some topological theories.* **Fundamenta Mathematicae,** vol. 38 (1950), pp. 137—152.

[66] A. Grzegorczyk. *Computable functionals.* **Fundamenta Mathematicae,** vol. 42 (1955), pp. 168—202.

[67] A. Grzegorczyk. *Elementarily definable analysis.* **Fundamenta Mathematicae,** vol. 41 (1955), pp. 311—338.

[68] A. Grzegorczyk. *Some proofs of undecidability of arithmetic.* **Fundamenta Mathematicae,** vol. 43 (1956) pp. 166—177.

[69] A. Grzegorczyk. *Recursive objects in all finite types.* **Fundamenta Mathematicae,** vol. 54 (1964), pp. 73—93.

[70] A. Grzegorczyk. *A philosophically plausible formal interpretation of intuitionistic logic.* **Indagationes Mathematicae,** vol. 26 (1964), pp. 596—601.

[71] A. Grzegorczyk, A. Mostowski and C. Ryll-Nardzewski. *The classical and the ω-complete arithmetic.* **Journal of Symbolic Logic,** vol. 23 (1958), pp. 188—206.

[72] J. D. Halpern. *The independence of the axiom of choice from the Boolean prime ideal theorem.* **Fundamenta Mathematicae,** vol. 55 (1964), pp. 57—66.

[73] W. Hanf. **Some fundamental problems concerning languages with infinitely long formulas.** Unpublished doctoral dissertation, University of California, 1962.

[74] K. Hauschild. *Ein Beitrag zur Metatheorie der Mengenlehre.* **Zeitschrift für mathematische Logik und Grundlagen der Mathematik,** vol. 9 (1963), pp. 291—314.

[75] G. Hasenjaeger. *Eine Bemerkung zu Henkin's Beweis für die Vollständigkeit des Prädikatenkalküls der ersten Stufe.* **Journal of Symbolic Logic,** vol. 18 (1953), pp. 42—48.

[76] L. Henkin. *The completeness of the first order functional calculus.* **Journal of Symbolic Logic,** vol. 14 (1949), pp. 159—166.

[77] L. Henkin. *Completeness in the theory of types.* **Journal of Symbolic Logic,** vol. 15 (1950), pp. 81—91.

[78] L. Henkin. *Some interconnections between modern algebra and mathematical logic.* **Transactions of the American Mathematical Society,** vol. 72 (1952), pp. 437—449.

[79] J. Herbrand. *Recherches sur la théorie de la démonstration.* **Travaux de la Société des Sciences et des Lettres de Varsovie,** Cl. III, no. 33 (1930), 128 pp.

[80] A. Heyting. *Die formalen Regeln der intuitionistischen Logik.* **Sitzungsberichte der Preussischen Akademie der Wissenschaften,** Phys. Math. Klasse, 1930, pp. 42—56.

[81] D. Hilbert and P. Bernays. **Grundlagen der Mathematik,** vol. 2. Springer, Berlin, 1939.

[82] J. Hintikka. *Form and content in quantification theory.* **Two papers on symbolic logic. Acta Philosophica Fennica,** vol. 8 (1955), pp. 7—55.

[83] J. Hintikka. *Reductions in the theory of types.* **Two papers on symbolic logic. Acta Philosophica Fennica,** vol. 8 (1955), pp. 61—115.

[84] A. Janiczak. *Undecidability of some simple formalized theories.* **Fundamenta Mathematicae,** vol. 40 (1953), pp. 131—139.

[85] S. Jaśkowski. *Recherches sur le système de la logique intuitionniste.* **Actes du Congrès International de Philosophie Scientifique,** vol. 6:

Philosophie des mathématiques. Hermann & Cie 1936, Paris, pp. 58—61.

[86] A. S. Kahr, E. F. Moore and H. Wang. *Entscheidungsproblem reduced to the* ∀∃∀ *case.* **Proceedings of the National Academy of Sciences of the U.S.A.,** vol. 48 (1962), pp. 365—377.

[87] C. R. Karp. **Languages with expressions of infinite length.** North-Holland Publishing Company, Amsterdam, 1964.

[88] J. H. Keisler. *Theory of models with generalized atomic formulas.* **Journal of Symbolic Logic,** vol. 25 (1960), pp. 1—26.

[89] J. H. Keisler. *Ultraproducts and elementary classes.* **Indagationes Mathematicae,** vol. 23 (1961), pp. 477—495.

[90] J. H. Keisler. *Isomorphism of ultraproducts II.* **Notices of the American Mathematical Society,** vol. 8 (1961), pp. 63—64.

[91] J. H. Keisler. *Some applications of the theory of models to set theory.* **Logic, Methodology and Philosophy of Science: Proceedings of the 1960 International Congress,** Stanford University Press, Stanford, California, 1962, pp. 80—86.

[92] H. J. Keisler and A. Tarski. *From accessible to inaccessible cardinals.* **Fundamenta Mathematicae,** vol. 53 (1964), pp. 225—308.

[93] J. G. Kemeny. *Type theory* vs. *set theory (abstract).* **Journal of Symbolic Logic,** vol. 15 (1950), p. 78.

[94] O. Ketonen. *Untersuchungen zum Prädikatenkalkül.* **Annales Academiae Scientiarum Fennicae,** ser. A I, vol. 23, Helsinki 1944, 71 pp.

[95] A. Kino and G. Takeuti. *On hierarchies of predicates of ordinal numbers.* **Journal of the Mathematical Society of Japan,** vol. 14 (1962), pp. 199—232.

[96] D. Klaua. **Konstruktive Analysis. Mathematische Forschungsberichte,** Berlin 1961.

[97] S. C. Kleene. *General recursive functions of natural numbers.* **Mathematische Annalen,** 112 (1936), pp. 727—742.

[98] S. C. Kleene. *Recursive predicates and quantifiers.* **Transactions of the American Mathematical Society,** vol. 53 (1943), pp. 41—73.

[99] S. C. Kleene. *On the interpretation of intuitionistic number theory.* **Journal of Symbolic Logic** vol. 10 (1945), pp. 109—124.

[100] S. C. Kleene. *A symmetric form of Gödel's theorem.* **Indagationes Mathematicae,** vol. 12 (1950), pp. 244—246.

[101] S. C. Kleene. *Permutability of inferences in Gentzen's calculi LK and LJ.* **Memoirs of the American Mathematical Society,** vol. 10 (1952), pp. 1—26.

[102] S. C. Kleene. *Recursive functions and intuitionistic mathematics.* **Proceedings of the International Congress of Mathematicians, Cambridge, Mass., 1950;** Providence, R. I., vol. 1 (1952), pp. 679—685.

[103] S. C. Kleene. *Finite axiomatizability of theories in the predicate calculus using additional predicate symbols. Two papers on the predicate calculus.* **Memoirs of the American Mathematical Society,** no. 10 (1952), pp. 27—66.

[104] S. C. Kleene. **Introduction to metamathematics.** North-Holland Publishing Company, Amsterdam, 1952.

[105] S. C. Kleene. *Arithmetical predicates and function quantifiers.* **Transactions of the American Mathematical Society,** vol. 79 (1955), pp. 312—340.

[106] S. C. Kleene. *Recursive functionals and quantifiers of finite types I.* **Transactions of the American Mathematical Society,** vol. 91 (1959), pp. 1—52.

[107] S. C. Kleene. *λ-definable functionals of finite types.* **Fundamenta Mathematicae,** vol. 50 (1962), pp. 281—303.

[108] S. C. Kleene. *Recursive functionals and quantifiers of finite types II.* **Transactions of the American Mathematical Society,** vol. 108 (1963), pp. 106—142.

[109] S. C. Kleene and E. L. Post. *The upper semi-lattice of degrees of insolvability.* **Annals of Mathematics,** vol. 59 (1954), pp. 379—407.

[109 a] S. C. Kleene and R. E. Vesley. **The foundations of intuitionistic mathematics.** North-Holland Publishing Company, Amsterdam 1965.

[110] S. Kochen. *Ultraproducts in the theory of models.* **Annals of Mathematics,** vol. 74 (1961), pp. 231—261.

[111] A. N. Kolmogorov. *Zur Deutung der intuitionistischen Logik.* **Mathematische Zeitschrift,** vol. 35 (1932), pp. 58—65.

[112] G. Kreisel. *A variant to Hilbert's theory of the foundations of arithmetic.* **The British Journal of the Philosophy of Science,** vol. 4 (1953—54), pp. 107—129. (Cf. *ibid.* p. 357.)

[113] G. Kreisel. *A remark on free choice sequences and the topological completeness proofs.* **Journal of Symbolic Logic,** vol. 23 (1958), pp. 369—388.

[114] G. Kreisel. *Set theoretic problems suggested by the notion of potential totality.* **Infinitistic Methods.** Pergamon Press and PWN, Oxford and Warszawa, 1959 pp. 103—140.

[115] G. Kreisel. *Analysis of the Cantor—Bendixon theorem by means of the analytic hierarchy.* **Bulletin de l'Académie Polonaise des Sciences,** série math., astr. et phys. vol. 7 (1959), pp. 621—626.

[116] G. Kreisel, D. Lacombe and J. R. Shoenfield. *Fonctionelles récursivement définissables et fonctionelles récursives.* **Comptes rendus de l'Académie des Sciences (Paris),** vol. 245 (1957), pp. 399—402.

[117] G. Kreisel and H. Wang. *Some applications of formalized consistency proofs.* **Fundamenta Mathematicae,** vol. 42 (1955), pp. 101—110.

[117 a] S. A. Kripke. *Semantical analysis of intuitionistic logic I.* **Formal Systems and Recursive Functions.** North-Holland Publishing Company, Amsterdam 1965, pp. 92—130.

[118] K. Kuratowski. *Ensembles projetifs et ensembles singuliers.* **Fundamenta Mathematicae,** vol. 35 (1948), pp. 131—140.

[119] A. H. Lachlan. *Recursive real numbers.* **Journal of Symbolic Logic,** vol. 28 (1963), pp. 1—16.

[120] D. Lacombe. *Extension de la notion de fonction récursive aux*

fonctions d'une ou plusieurs variables. **Comptes rendus de l'Académie des Sciences (Paris),** vol. 240 (1955), pp. 2478—2480, vol. 241 (1955), pp. 13—14 and 151—153.

[121] H. Läuchli. *The independence of the ordering principle from a restricted axiom of choice.* **Fundamenta Mathematicae,** vol. 54 (1964) pp. 31—43.

[122] A. Lévy. *Axiom schemata of strong infinity in axiomatic set theory.* **Pacific Journal of Mathematics,** vol. 10 (1960), pp. 223—238.

[123] A. Lévy. *The Fraenkel-Mostowski method for independence proofs in set theory.* **Proceedings of the 1963 Symposium on Model Theory in Berkeley, California.** North-Holland Publishing Company, Amsterdam. Forthcoming.

[123 a] E. K. G. Lopez-Escobar. *Universal formulas in the infinitary language $L_{\alpha\beta}$* **Bulletin de l'Académie Polonaise des Sciences,** série math., astr. et phys., vol. 13 (1965), forthcoming.

[124] P. Lorenzen. *Ein dialogisches Konstruktivitätskriterium.* **Infinitistic Methods.** Pergamon Press and PWN, Oxford and Warszawa, 1959, pp. 193—200.

[125] J. Łoś. *Sur le théorème de Gödel pour les théories indénombrables.* **Bulletin de l'Académie Polonaise des Sciences** Cl. III, vol. 2 (1954), pp. 319—320.

[126] J. Łoś. *On the categoricity in power of elementary deductive systems and some related problems.* **Colloquium Mathematicum,** vol. 3 (1954), pp. 58—62.

[127] J. Łoś. *On the extending of models I.* **Fundamenta Mathematicae,** vol. 42 (1955), pp. 38—54.

[128] J. Łoś. *Quelques remarques, thèorèmes et problèmes sur les classes définissables d'algebres.* **Mathematical interpretations of formal systems.** North-Holland Publishing Company, Amsterdam, 1955, pp. 98—113.

[129] J. Łoś and Cz. Ryll-Nardzewski. *Effectiveness of the representation theory for Boolean algebras.* **Fundamenta Mathematicae,** vol. 41 (1955), pp. 49—56.

[130] J. Łoś and R. Suszko. *On the extending of models IV. Infinite sums of models.* **Fundamenta Mathematicae,** vol. 44 (1957), pp. 52—60.

[131] R. C. Lyndon. *Properties preserved under algebraic constructions.* **Bulletin of the American Mathematical Society,** vol. 65 (1959), pp. 287—299.

[132] R. MacDowell and E. Specker. *Modelle der Arithmetik.* **Infinitistic Methods.** Pergamon Press and PWN, Oxford and Warszawa, 1959, pp. 257—263.

[133] M. Machover. *The theory of transfinite recursion.* **Bulletin of the American Mathematical Society,** vol. 67 (1961), pp. 575—578.

[134] A. I. Malcev. *Untersuchungen aus dem Gebiet der mathematischen Logik.* **Matematičeskij Sbornik n.s.,** vol. 1 (1936), pp. 323—336.

[135] A. I. Malcev. *Ob odnom obščem métodé polučeniá lokalnyh téorém féorii grupp* (On a general method for obtaining local theorems in group

theory). Ivanovskij Gosudarstvénnyj Pédagogičéskij Institut. **Učenyé Zapiski, Fiziko matématičéskié Nauki**, vol. 1 (1941), pp. 3—9.

[136] A. I. Malcev. *Konstruktivnyé algébry I* (Constructive algebras I). **Uspéhy matématičeskih Nauk**, vol. 16 (1961), pp. 3—60.

[137] E. Marczewski. *Sur les congruences et les propriétés positives d'algèbres abstraites.* **Colloquium Mathematicum**, vol. 2 (1951), pp. 220—228.

[138] A. A. Markov. *Névozmožnosť nékotoryh algorifmov v téorii associativnyh sistém* (Impossibility of certain algorithms in the theory of associative systems). **Doklady Akadémii Nauk SSSR**, vol. 55 (1947), pp. 587—590.

[139] A. A. Markov. *Teoria algorifmov.* **Trudy Matématičéskogo Instituta iméni V. A. Stéklova**, vol. 42 (1954), 375 pp.

[140] A. A. Markov. *O konstruktivnyh funkciáh* (On constructive functions). **Trudy Matématičéskogo Instituta iméni V. A. Stéklova**, vol. 52 (1958), pp. 315—348.

[141] S. Mazur. *Computable analysis* (edited by A. Grzegorczyk and H. Rasiowa). **Rozprawy Matematyczne**, vol. 33 (1963), pp. 1—111.

[142] J. C. C. McKinsey and A. Tarski. *Closed elements in closure algebras.* **Annals of Mathematics**, ser. 2, vol. 47 (1946), pp. 122—162.

[143] E. Mendelson. *The independence of a weak axiom of choice.* **Journal of Symbolic Logic**, vol. 21 (1956), pp. 350—366.

[144] R. Montague. *Semantical closure and non-finite axiomatizability I.* **Infinitistic methods.** Pergamon Press and PWN, Oxford and Warszawa 1959, pp. 45—69.

[145] R. Montague. *Non-finite axiomatizability.* **Summaries of talks presented at the Summer Institute of Symbolic Logic, Cornell University 1957.** Second edition, Princeton University Press, Princeton, N. J., (1960), pp. 256—259.

[146] R. Montague. *Reductions of higher order logics.* **Proceedings of the 1963 Symposium on model theory in Berkeley, California.** North-Holland Publishing Company, Amsterdam. Forthcoming.

[147] M. Morley. *On theories categorical in uncountable powers.* **Proceedings of the National Academy of Sciences of the U.S.A.**, vol. 49 (1963), pp. 213—216.

[148] M. Morley. *Omitting classes of elements.* **Proceedings of the 1963 Symposium on model theory in Berkeley, California.** North-Holland Publishing Company, Amsterdam. Forthcoming.

[149] A. Mostowski. *On absolute properties of relations.* **Journal of Symbolic Logic**, vol. 12 (1947), pp. 33—42.

[150] A. Mostowski. *On models of axiomatic systems.* **Fundamenta Mathematicae**, vol. 39 (1952), pp. 133—158.

[151] A. Mostowski. *Concerning a problem of H. Scholz.* **Zeitschrift für mathematische Logik und Grundlagen der Mathematik**, vol. 2 (1956), pp. 210—214.

[152] A. Mostowski. *Concerning the problem of axiomatizability of the*

field of real numbers in the weak second order logic. **Essays on the foundations of mathematics,** Magnes Press, Jerusalem 1961, pp. 269—286.

[153] A. A. Mučnik. *Nérazrešimost' problémy svodimosti téorii algorifmov* (Negative answer to the problem of reducibility of the theory of algorithms). **Doklady Akadémii Nauk SSSR,** vol. 108 (1956), pp. 194—197.

[154] J. Myhill. *Creative sets.* **Zeitschrift für Mathematische Logik und Grundlagen der Mathematik,** vol. 1 (1955), pp. 97—108.

[155] J. Myhill and J. C. Shepherdson. *Effective operations on partial recursive functions.* **Zeitschrift für mathematische Logik und Grundlagen der Mathematik,** vol. 1 (1955), pp. 310—317.

[156] Ilse L. Novak. *A construction for models of consistent systems.* **Fundamenta Mathematicae,** vol. 37 (1950), pp. 87—110.

[157] P. S. Novikov. *O néprotivoréčivosti nékotoryh položénij déskriptivnoj téorii množéstv.* (On the consistency of some theorems of the descriptive theory of sets). **Trudy Matématičéskogo Instituta iméni V. A. Stéklova,** vol. 28 (1951), pp. 279—316.

[158] P. S. Novikov. *Ob algoritmičeskoj nérazrešimosti problémy toždéstva slov v téorii grupp.* (Algorithmic unsolvability of the word problem in group theory). **Trudy Matématičéskogo Instituta iméni V. A. Stéklova,** vol. 44 (1955), 143 pp.

[159] R. Péter. **Rekursive Funktionen.** Akadémiai Kiado, Budapest 1951.

[160] E. L. Post. *Recursively enumerable sets of positive integers and their decision problems.* **Bulletin of the American Mathematical Society,** vol. 50 (1944), pp. 284—316.

[161] E. L. Post. *Recursive unsolvability of a problem of Thue.* **Journal of Symbolic Logic,** vol. 12 (1947), pp. 1—11.

[162] H. Putnam. *Decidability and essential undecidability.* **Journal of Symbolic Logic,** vol. 22 (1957), pp. 39—54.

[163] H. Putnam. *Trial and error predicates and the solution to a problem of Mostowski's.* **Journal of Symbolic Logic,** vol. 30 (1965), pp. 49—58.

[164] W. V. O. Quine. **Mathematical logic.** Harvard University Press, Cambridge, Mass., 1940.

[165] M. O. Rabin. *On recursively enumerable and arithmetic models of set theory.* **Journal of Symbolic Logic,** vol. 23 (1958), pp. 408—416.

[166] M. O. Rabin. *Arithmetical extensions with prescribed cardinality.* **Proceedings of the Royal Academy of Sciences,** Amsterdam, Ser. A, vol. 62 (1959), pp. 439—446.

[167] M. O. Rabin. *Non standard models and the induction axiom.* **Essays on the foundations of mathematics.** Magnes Press, Jerusalem, 1961, pp. 287—291.

[168] M. O. Rabin. *Computable algebra. General theory and theory of commutative fields.* **Transactions of the American Mathematical Society,** vol. 95 (1962), pp. 341—360.

[169] M. O. Rabin. *Universal groups of automorphisms of models.* **Proceedings of the 1963 Symposium on Model Theory in Berkeley,**

California. North-Holland Publishing Company, Amsterdam. Forthcoming.

[170] M. O. Rabin. *A direct method for undecidability proofs.* **Proceedings of the 1964 International Congress of Logic, Methodology, and Philosophy of Science in Jerusalem.** North-Holland Publishing Company, Amsterdam. Forthcoming.

[171] H. Rasiowa. *Algebraic treatment of the functional calculi of Heyting and Lewis.* **Fundamenta Mathematicae,** vol. 38 (1951), pp. 99—126.

[172] H. Rasiowa and R. Sikorski. *A proof of the completeness theorem of Gödel.* **Fundamenta Mathematicae,** vol. 37 (1950), pp. 193—200

[173] H. Rasiowa and R. Sikorski. **The mathematics of metamathematics.** PWN, Warszawa, 1963.

[174] H. G. Rice. *Recursive real numbers.* **Proceedings of the American Mathematical Society,** vol. 5 (1954), pp. 784—791.

[175] L. Rieger. *On free $\aleph_\xi$-complete Boolean algebras (with an application to logic).* **Fundamenta Mathematicae,** vol. 38 (1951), pp. 35—52.

[176] J. Robinson. *Definability and decision problems in arithmetic.* **Journal of Symbolic Logic,** vol. 14 (1949), pp. 98—114.

[177] J. Robinson. *General recursive functions.* **Proceedings of the American Mathematical Society,** vol. 1 (1951), pp. 703—718.

[178] R. M. Robinson. Review of [159]. **Journal of Symbolic Logic,** vol. 16 (1951), pp. 280—282.

[179] R. M. Robinson. *Undecidable rings.* **Transactions of the American Mathematical Society,** vol. 70 (1951), pp. 137—159.

[180] A. Robinson. *Ordered structures and related concepts.* **Mathematical interpretation of formal systems.** North-Holland Publishing Company, Amsterdam, 1955, pp. 51—56.

[181] A. Robinson. *Solution of a problem of Tarski.* **Fundamenta Mathematicae,** vol. 47 (1959), pp. 179—204.

[182] A. Robinson. *Non-standard analysis.* **Proceedings of the Royal Academy of Sciences,** Amsterdam, ser. A, vol. 64 (1961), pp. 432—440.

[183] A. Robinson. **Introduction to model theory and to the metamathematics of algebra.** North-Holland Publishing Company, Amsterdam 1963.

[184] H. Rogers Jr. *Certain logical reductions and decision problems.* **Annals of Mathematics,** vol. 64 (1956), pp. 264—284.

[185] H. Rogers Jr. *Computing degrees of unsolvability.* **Mathematische Annalen,** vol. 138 (1959), pp. 125—140.

[186] G. F. Rose. *Propositional calculus and realizability.* **Transactions of the American Mathematical Society,** vol. 75 (1953), pp. 1—19.

[187] J. B. Rosser. *Extensions of some theorems of Gödel and Church.* **Journal of Symbolic Logic,** vol. 1 (1936), pp. 87—91.

[188] Cz. Ryll-Nardzewski. *On theories categorical in power* $\leq \aleph_0$. **Bulletin de l'Académie Polonaise des Sciences,** série math., astr. et phys. vol. 7 (1959), pp. 545—548.

[189] Cz. Ryll-Nardzewski. *The role of the axiom of induction in*

elementary arithmetic. **Fundamenta Mathematicae,** vol. 39 (1952), pp. 239—263.

[190] G. E. Sacks. **Degrees of unsolvability.** Princeton University Press, Princeton, N.J., 1963.

[191] N. A. Šanin. *O konstruktivnom matématičéskom analizé.* (On the constructive mathematical analysis). **Trudy trétégo matématicéskogo Sézda.** Moscow 1956, pp. 69—71.

[192] N. A. Šanin. *Nékotoryé voprosy matématičéskogo analiza v svété konstruktivnoj logiki.* (Einige Fragen der Analysis im Lichte der konstruktiven Logik). **Zeitschrift für mathematische Logik und Grundlagen der Mathematik,** vol. 2 (1956), pp. 27—36.

[193] B. Scarpellini. *Die Nichtaxiomatisierbarkeit des unendlichwertigen Prädikatenkalküls von Łukasiewicz.* **Journal of Symbolic Logic,** vol. 27 (1963), pp. 159—170.

[194] H. Scholz. *Problem No. 1.* **Journal of Symbolic Logic,** vol. 17 (1952), p. 160.

[195] K. Schütte. *Beweistheoretische Erfassung der unendlichen Induktion in der Zahlentheorie.* **Mathematische Annalen,** vol. 122 (1951), pp. 369—389.

[195 a] K. Schütte. *Ein System des verknüpfenden Schliessens.* **Archiv für mathematische Logik und Grundlagenforschung,** vol. 2 (1956), pp., 56—67

[195 b] K. Schütte. **Beweistheorie.** Springer, Berlin 1960.

[196] D. Scott. *On constructing models for arithmetic.* **Infinitistic methods.** Pergamon Press and PWN, Oxford and Warszawa 1959, pp. 235—255.

[197] D. Scott. *Completeness proofs for the intuitionistic sentential calculus.* **Summaries of talks presented at the Summer Institute for Symbolic Logic. Cornell University 1957.** Second edition. Princeton University Press, Princeton 1960.

[198] D. Scott. *Measurable cardinals and constructible sets.* **Bulletin de l'Académie Polonaise des Sciences,** série math., astr. et phys., vol. 9 (1961), pp. 521—524.

[199] D. Scott. *Logic with denumerably long formulas and finitary quantifiers.* **Proceedings of the 1963 Symposium on model theory in Berkeley, California.** North-Holland Publishing Company, Amsterdam. Forthcoming.

[200] D. Scott and A. Tarski. *The sentential calculus with infinitely long expressions.* **Colloquium Mathematicum,** vol. 6 (1958), pp. 165—170.

[201] J. C. Shepherdson. *Inner models for set theory. Part III.* **Journal of Symbolic Logic,** vol. 18 (1953), pp. 145—167.

[202] J. R. Shoenfield. *A relative consistency proof.* **Journal of Symbolic Logic,** vol. 19 (1954), pp. 21—28.

[203] J. R. Shoenfield. *The independence of the axiom of choice* (abstract). **Journal of Symbolic Logic,** vol. 20 (1955), p. 202.

[204] J. R. Shoenfield. *On a restricted ω-rule.* **Bulletin de l'Académie Polonaise des Sciences,** série math., astr. et phys. vol. 7 (1959), pp. 405—407.

[205] J. R. Shoenfield. *An uncountable set of incomparable degrees.* **Proceedings of the American Mathematical Society,** vol. 11 (1960), pp. 61—62.

[206] J. R. Shoenfield. *Undecidable and creative theories.* **Fundamenta Mathematicae,** vol. 49 (1960—61), pp. 171—179.

[207] J. R. Shoenfield. *The problem of predicativity.* **Essays in foundations of mathematics.** Magnes Press, Jerusalem 1961, pp. 132—139.

[208] Th. Skolem. *Untersuchungen über die Axiome des Klassenkalküls und über die Produktations- und Summationsprobleme, welche gewisse Klassen von Aussagen betreffen.* **Skrifter utgit av Videskapsselskapet i Kristiania,** I Klasse, no. 3, 1919.

[209] Th. Skolem. *Über die Nichtcharakterisierbarkeit der Zahlenreihe mittels endlich oder abzählbar unendlichvieler Aussagen mit ausschliesslich Zahlenvariablen.* **Fundamenta Mathematicae,** vol. 23 (1934), pp. 150 —161.

[210] R. Sikorski. *Der Heytingsche Prädikatenkalkül und metrische Räume.* **Constructivity in Mathematics.** North-Holland Publishing Company, Amsterdam, 1959, pp. 250—253.

[211] E. Specker. *Nichtkonstruktiv beweisbare Sätze der Analysis.* **Journal of Symbolic Logic,** vol. 14 (1949), pp. 145—158.

[212] E. Specker. *Der Satz vom Maximum in der rekursiven Analysis.* **Constructivity in Mathematics.** North-Holland Publishing Company. Amsterdam, 1959, pp. 254—265.

[213] E. Specker. *Eine Verschärfung des Unvollständigkeitssatzes der Zahlentheorie.* **Bulletin de l'Académie Polonaise des Sciences,** Cl. III, vol. 5 (1957), pp. 1043—1047.

[214] E. Specker. *Zur Axiomatik der Mengenlehre (Fundierung und Auswahlaxiom).* **Zeitschrift für Mathematische Logik und Grundlagen der Mathematik,** vol. 3 (1957), pp. 173—210.

[215] C. Spector. *On degrees of recursive unsolvability.* **Annals of Mathematics,** vol. 64 (1956), pp. 581—592.

[215a]. C. Spector. *Recursive well-orderings.* **Journal of Symbolic Logic,** vol. 20 (1955), pp. 151—162.

[216] C. Spector. *Provably recursive functionals of analysis: a consistency proof of analysis by an extension of principles formulated in current intuitionistic mathematics.* **Recursive function theory. Proceedings of Symposia in Pure Mathematics,** vol. 5 (1962), pp. 1—27.

[217] M. H. Stone. *The theory of representations of Boolean algebras.* **Transactions of the American Mathematical Society,** vol. 40 (1936), pp. 37—111.

[218] M. H. Stone. *Topological representations of distributive lattices and Brouwerian logics.* **Časopis pro pěstovani matematiky a fysiky,** vol. 67 (1937—8), pp. 1—25.

[219] J. Surányi. **Reduktionstheorie des Entscheidungsproblems im Prädikatenkalkül der ersten Stufe.** Ungarische Akademie der Wissenschaften, Budapest 1959.

[219a] L. Svenonius. $\aleph_0$-*categoricity in first-order predicate calculus.* **Theoria,** vol. 25 (1959), pp. 82—94.

[220] W. Szmielew. *Elementary properties of abelian groups*. **Fundamenta Mathematicae**, vol. 41 (1953), pp. 203—271.

[221] A. D. Tajmanov. *Haraktéristiki aksiomatiziruémyh klassov modéléj* (Characterizations of axiomatizable classes of models). **Algébra i Logika.** Seminar. Novosibirsk, vol. 1 (1962), pp. 5—44.

[222] A. Tarski. **Der Wahrheitsbegriff in formalisierten Sprachen. Studia Philosophica,** vol. 1 (1936), pp. 261—405. [Polish original appeared in Prace Towarzystwa Naukowego Warszawskiego, Wydzial III, no. 34 (1933), pp. VII + 116].

[223] A. Tarski. *Einige methodologische Untersuchungen über die Definierbarkeit der Begriffe.* **Erkenntnis,** vol. 5 (1935—36), pp. 80—100 [Polish original appeared in Przegląd Filozoficzny 37 (1934), pp. 438 —460].

[224] A. Tarski. *Über unerreichbare Kardinalzahlen.* **Fundamenta Mathematicae,** vol. 30 (1938), pp. 68—89.

[225] A. Tarski. *Der Aussagenkalkül und die Topologie.* **Fundamenta Mathematicae,** vol. 31 (1938), pp. 103—104.

[226] A. Tarski. **A decision method for elementary algebra and geometry.** Second edition. University of California Press, Berkeley, California, 1951.

[227] A. Tarski. *Some notions and methods on the borderline of algebra and metamathematics.* **Proceedings of the International Congress of Mathematicians, Cambridge, Mass., 1950;** Providence, R. I., vol. 1, 1952, pp. 705—720.

[228] A. Tarski. *Contributions to the theory of models I and II.* **Indagationes Mathematicae,** vol. 16 (1954), pp. 572—588, and vol. 17 (1955), pp. 56—64.

[229] A. Tarski. *Some model-theoretic results concerning weak second order logic.* **Notices of the American Mathematical Society,** vol. 5 (1958), abstract 550—6.

[230] A. Tarski. *Some problems and results relevant to the foundations of set theory.* **Logic, Methodology and Philosophy of Science. Proceedings of the 1960 International Congress,** Stanford University Press, Stanford, California, 1962, pp. 125—136.

[231] A. Tarski, A. Mostowski and R. M. Robinson. **Undecidable theories.** North Holland Publishing Company, Amsterdam, 1953.

[232] A. Tarski and R. L. Vaught. *Arithmetical extensions of relational systems.* **Compositio Mathematica,** vol. 13 (1957), pp. 81—102.

[233] B. A. Trachténbrot. *Névozmožnosť algorifma dlá problémy razrešimosti na konéčnyh klassah.* (Impossibility of an algorithm for the decision problem in finite classes). **Doklady Akademii Nauk SSSR,** vol. 70 (1950), pp. 569—572.

[234] A. M. Turing. *On computable numbers, with an application to the Entscheidungsproblem.* **Proceedings of the London Mathematical Society,** Series 2, vol. 42 (1936—1937), pp. 230—265.

[235] A. M. Turing. *Systems of logic based on ordinals.* **Proceedings of the London Mathematical Society,** Series 2, vol. 45 (1939), pp. 161—228.

[236] R. L. Vaught. *Applications of the Löwenheim—Skolem—Tarski theorem to problems of completeness and decidability.* **Indagationes Mathematicae,** vol. 16 (1954), pp. 467—472.

[237] R. L. Vaught. *Denumerable models of complete theories.* **Infinitisticmethods.** Pergamon Press and PWN, Oxford and Warszawa, 1959, pp. 303—321.

[238] R. L. Vaught. *Sentences true in all constructive models.* **Journal of Symbolic Logic,** vol. 25 (1960), pp. 39—53.

[239] R. L. Vaught. *The completeness of logic with the added quantifier "there are uncountably many".* **Fundamenta Mathematicae,** vol. 54 (1964), pp. 303—304.

[239 a] R. L. Vaught. *Models of complete theories.* **Bulletin of the American Mathematical Society,** vol. 69 (1963), pp. 299—313.

[240] B. L. v.d. Waerden. *Eine Bemerkung über die Unzerlegbarkeit der Polynomen.* **Mathematische Annalen,** vol. 102 (1930), pp. 738—739.

[241] H. Wang. *The irreducibility of impredicative principles.* **Mathematische Annalen,** vol. 125 (1952), pp. 56—66.

[242] H. Wang. *Undecidable sentences generated by semantic paradoxes.* **Journal of Symbolic Logic,** vol. 20 (1955), pp. 31—43.

[243] H. Wang. **A survey of mathematical logic.** North-Holland Publishing Company, Amsterdam, 1963. (See pp. 507—534.)

[244] H. Weyl. *The ghost of modality.* **Philosophical essays in memory of Edmund Husserl.** Harvard University Press, Cambridge, Mass., 1940, pp. 278—303.

Index of Authors

Index of Subjects

ACTA PHILOSOPHICA FENNICA

Obtainable from Akateeminen Kirjakauppa —
The Academic Bookstore, Helsinki
and from all academic booksellers.